Level 6

Building
VOCABULARY
from Word Roots

Guided
Practice
Book

adventure

native

confection

Authors

Timothy Rasinski, Nancy Padak, Rick M. Newton, and Evangeline Newton

Teacher Created Materials
PUBLISHING

Credits

Editor
Christine Dugan, M.A. Ed.

Assistant Editor
Leslie Huber, M.A.

Senior Editor
Lori Kamola, M.S. Ed.

Editor-in-Chief
Sharon Coan, M.S. Ed.

Editorial Manager
Gisela Lee, M.A.

Creative Director
Lee Aucoin

Cover Design
Lee Aucoin

Imaging
Deb Brown
Robin Erickson
Don Tran
Phil Garcia

ELL Consultants
Melina E. Castillo, Ed.D.
Bilingual Curriculum Supervisor
Division of Bilingual Education
and World Languages
Miami-Dade County Public Schools

Carmen Zuñiga Dunlap, Ph.D.
Associate Dean, College of Education
California State University, Fullerton

Karie A. Feldner, M.S. Ed.

Maria Elvira Gallardo, M.A.

Publisher
Rachelle Cracchiolo, M.S. Ed.

To order additional copies of this book or any other Teacher Created Materials products, go to www.tcmpub.com or call 1-800-585-7339.

Teacher Created Materials

5301 Oceanus Drive
Huntington Beach, CA 92649-1030
http://www.tcmpub.com
ISBN 978-1-4258-0656-9
© 2007 Teacher Created Materials
Reprinted, 2008
Made in U.S.A.

Part A:
Meet the Root

Divide and Conquer

Directions: "Divide" words and then "conquer" them by writing the meaning of the words. Use the Root Bank at the bottom of the page to help you remember what each of the parts means.

	base means	suffix means	word means
1. expose	_____	_____	_____
2. inscribe	_____	_____	_____
3. transpose	_____	_____	_____
4. prescribe	_____	_____	_____
5. predict	_____	_____	_____
6. concur	_____	_____	_____
7. elect	_____	_____	_____
8. progress	_____	_____	_____
9. pyrophobia	_____	_____	_____
10. dictate	_____	_____	_____

Root Bank

Prefixes: *con-* = "with, together"; *e-, ex-* = "out"; *in-* = "in, on, into"; *pre-* = "before"; *pro-* = "forward"; *trans-* = "across, change"

Bases: *cur, curs, cour, cours* = "run, go"; *dict* = "say, tell, speak"; *grad, gress* = "step, go"; *leg, lig, lect* = "pick, choose, read"; *pon, pos, posit* = "put, place"; *pyro* = "fire"; *scrib, script* = "write"

Suffixes: *-phobia* = "fear of"; *-ate* = "to make or do"

Part B:
Combine and Create

Syllable Sort

Directions: Look at these words. Put them on the chart where they belong.

carbohydrates   hydrogen   pedestrian   monosyllables
contemporaries   synchronize   solitaire   pedigree
aquarium

three syllables	four syllables	five or more syllables

Part C:
Read and Reason

News Report

Directions: Read the following news report and answer the questions.

TOP NEWS!

Today in Hollywood, California, two animated characters came to life and fled their production sites. Police speculate that they might be dangerous, and the investigation is centered around a tip from an anonymous caller who said that the "toons" were recently spotted near the Mississippi River—a plot piece in last week's episode, "Down the Mountain, Oh River." Police are currently generating a search team to advance on the river and its outlets.

Questions:

Explain the meaning of *animated* in the above news report.

_____

What does it mean to *speculate?* _____

_____

Who is *speculating* in the above report?_____

What are the police *generating?* _____

Part D:
Extend and Explore

Making Words

Directions: Work with a partner. Fill in the chart with as many words as you can.

	struct	*struction*	*structive*
con-			
de-			
in-			
ob-			
recon-			

Now make three sentences with these words. See if you can put more than one word in a sentence. Make sure that your sentences make sense.

1. _____

    _____

2. _____

    _____

3. _____

    _____

Part E:
Go for the Gold!

Sixteen Square Wordo

Directions: Choose a free box and mark it. Then choose words from the list and write one word in each box. Your teacher will give you these words. You can choose the box for each word. Then your teacher will give a clue for each word. Mark an X in the box for each word you match to the clue. If you get four words in a row, column, diagonal, or four corners, call out, "Wordo!"

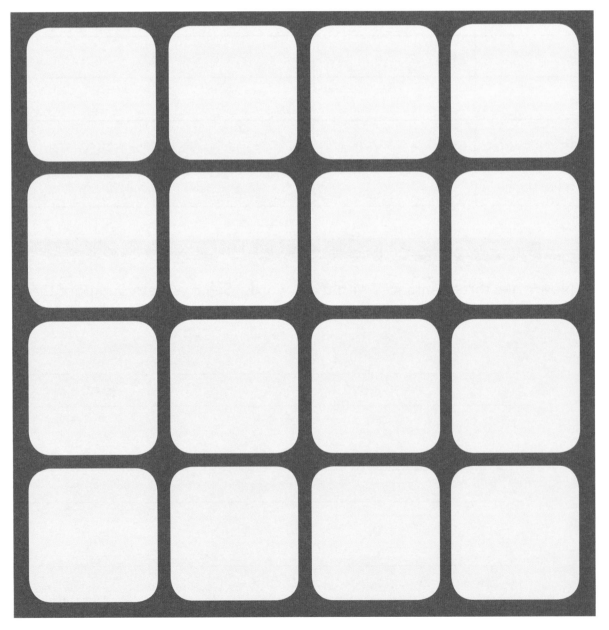

Part A:
Meet the Root

Divide and Conquer

Directions: "Divide" words and then "conquer" them by writing the meaning of the words. An X means the word does not have a base.

	prefix means	base means	word means
1. postscript		*script* = write	
2. postdate		*date* = date	
3. antecedent		*ced* = go	
4. antebellum		*bellum* = war	
5. postbellum		*bellum* = war	
6. posthumous		*hum* = burial in earth	
7. posterity		X	
8. antiquity		X	
9. postpone		*pone* = put, place	
10. ante meridiem (A.M.)		*Meridiem = mid-day*	

DID YOU KNOW?

When we say the time of day is A.M. or P.M. we are using abbreviations of Latin words. The word *meridiem* is Latin for "middle of the day" (*meri* = mid; *diem* = day). The abbreviation A.M. stands for *ante meridiem* and means "before midday." The abbreviation P.M. stands for *post meridiem* and means after midday. What time is midday?

Part B:
Combine and Create

Sorting Words

Directions: Sometimes *ante-* and *post-* mean "before" and "after." Sometimes they don't. Put the words on the chart where they belong.

anterior   anteater   antenna   antedate   antecedent
posture   postmodern   posterior   poster   postage
antelope   postpone

means "before" or "after"	does not mean "before" or "after"

DID YOU KNOW?

Have you ever written a letter and then thought of something you should have included? Chances are, you wrote a P.S. and added it. You probably did not know, however, that the abbreviation P.S. comes from the Latin phrase *post scriptum. Post* means "after" and *script* means "to write." A *postscript,* or P.S., indicates a thought that is added "after" a letter has been completely "written."

Part C:
Read and Reason

Dialogue

Directions: Read the following dialogue and see if you can find a picture to
draw that will represent one of the italicized words in context.

David: "I hope the *pregame* show goes quickly."

Elvira: "Why? It's only 10:00 am. Why hurry the day away for the big game?"

David: "I don't want to *postpone* the excitement any more. I'm ready to cheer
my team on to victory, especially during the *postgame* show."

Draw your picture here

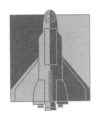

Part D:
Extend and Explore

Word Skits

Directions: Work with a partner. First, pick a word from the list below or from the "Divide and Conquer" activity. Then write it on an index card. Also write what it means, and write an example of when you might see it. Tell classmates what root you have used. Then act out the example of when you might see the word. See if your classmates can guess the word.

antique   postgame   show   postpone   a picnic

posterity (generations that come after us)

Part E:
Go for the Gold!

Word Search

Directions: Find the words listed below in the puzzle. Words can be across, down, on a diagonal, or backwards. Be careful! Some words start with the same letters.

ANTECEDENT   ANTEDATE   ANTERIOR
ANTIQUATED   ANTIQUE   POSTERIOR
POSTERITY   POSTGAME   POSTPONE
POSTSCRIPT

X	P	X	E	V	D	I	A	M	H	A	W	P	F	C
G	O	Y	C	D	Y	L	F	N	N	G	M	O	N	K
X	S	F	O	P	H	G	W	T	T	M	N	S	H	C
I	T	R	U	K	I	E	I	A	P	E	A	T	G	F
U	S	C	O	R	F	Q	G	D	I	N	D	G	K	N
Y	C	O	D	I	U	P	E	H	T	S	G	A	U	H
P	R	R	C	E	R	N	P	E	X	Z	Y	M	T	S
S	I	S	K	C	O	E	C	B	M	Z	T	E	A	E
I	P	Q	V	P	D	E	T	A	U	Q	I	T	N	A
R	T	E	T	Y	D	I	B	S	O	P	R	M	P	G
U	G	S	Q	E	H	L	I	L	O	Z	E	I	C	G
R	O	A	N	T	E	R	I	O	R	P	T	F	T	R
P	O	T	L	V	J	Q	Q	Y	Z	F	S	W	P	E
J	S	P	A	T	X	F	U	T	B	E	O	R	W	S
N	A	C	O	R	R	X	Z	C	R	U	P	W	C	E

Part A:
Meet the Root

Divide and Conquer

Directions: "Divide" words and then "conquer" them by writing the meaning of the words.

	prefix means	base means	word means
1. obstruct	in the way	*struct* = build	to build in the way of something
2. offend		*fend* = strike	
3. obstacle		*sta* = stand	
4. opponent		*pon* = put, place	
5. opposite		*posit* = put, place	
6. offer		*fer* = bring, bear	
7. observe		*serv* = keep watch	
8. objection		*ject* = throw	
9. obnoxious		*nox* = harm	
10. occurence		*cur* = run, go	

DID YOU KNOW?

The word *obsession*, which in Latin means "state of siege," comes to us from an ancient Roman war strategy. Roman soldiers conquered a town or fortress by "sitting" *(sess)* "up against" *(ob-)* the enemy's walls. This blockade, or "siege," cut people off from the world and forced them to surrender. Although the English words *obsess*, *obsessive*, and *obsession* no longer convey a military meaning, they still contain the concept of a siege. An *obsession* is a persistent thought or fear that "sits" "up against you" and will not let you relax.

Part B:
Combine and Create

Solving Riddles

Directions: Solve the riddles.

1. I have two syllables.
   I am a verb.
   I mean "to watch carefully" or "to keep a close watch over."

   _____

2. I am a noun.
   I have two syllables, but I have several meanings.
   I can mean "the act of doing something wrong."
   I can also mean the act of attacking, even in a football game.

   _____

3. I am an adjective.
   I have three syllables.
   I am a fancy way of saying "stubborn."

   _____

Part C:
Read and Reason

Advice Column

Directions: Read the following advice column and answer the questions.

Dear Adelia Advice,

Yesterday I was obnoxious. I tried to jump out of bed, but instead I landed on my brother, and I ended up breaking my leg. The day before that I tried to obscure the truth from my mother, and she found out I really did steal some cookies from the jar. And three days ago, I offended an older lady when I jumped in a puddle and splashed water all over everyone. I need some help learning to calm down.

Obnoxious Oliver

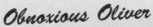

Dear Obnoxious Oliver,

Gee wiz! I would say you owe some people some apologies, so that's where I would start if I were you. Also, some of the best advice I've ever received is to "look before you leap." In other words, try thinking before you act. That might help you cut down on some obnoxious behaviors.

Adelia Advice

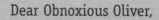

Questions:

1. Why does Oliver think he is obnoxious? _____

_____

2. What does it mean to "obscure the truth"? _____

_____

3. How does Oliver "offend" the older lady? _____

_____

Part D:
Extend and Explore

Making Riddles

Directions: Work with a partner. Make riddles for a few of the words on the list. Then trade riddles with another group. See if they can solve your riddles.

obstruction   observation   occupy   objection   obnoxious

1. _____

   _____

   Solution: _____

2. _____

   _____

   Solution: _____

3. _____

   _____

   Solution: _____

Part E:
Go for the Gold!

Crossword Puzzle

Directions: Read the clues below. Fill in the crossword puzzle with the correct words.

Across

1. excessive preoccupation
2. closure or blockage
5. to see or notice
6. hard to understand
7. annoying

Down

1. stubborn
3. something presented to be accepted or turned down
4. a place to look at stars and planets
5. to happen
8. act of exercising cruel power over others

Part A:
Meet the Root

Divide and Conquer

Directions: "Divide" words and then "conquer" them by writing the meaning of the words.
Note: The Latin base in numbers 3 and 9 is *i, it*, which means "go."

	prefix means	base means	word means
1. amphibian	_____	*bi(o)* = live, life	_____
2. ambidextrous	_____	*dextr* = right hand	_____
3. ambition	_____	*(i)t* = go	_____
4. ambivalent	_____	*val* = be strong	_____
5. amphitheater	_____	*theater* = theater, watch	_____
6. ambiguous	_____	*(i)gu* = drive	_____
7. amphibious	_____	*bi(o)* = live, life	_____
8. ambidexterity	_____	*dextr* = right hand	_____
9. ambience	_____	*(i)t* = go	_____
10. ambiguity	_____	*(i)gu* = drive	_____

DID YOU KNOW?

We use the word *ambition* to describe someone who works hard to "get ahead." How does that meaning come from "around" or "on both sides"? In ancient Rome, a candidate running for public office always wore a white toga (*candid* in Latin means "white"). The candidate would go "around" and greet people as he tried to win their votes. A candidate with political *ambitions* could be seen in his white toga, greeting the people "on both sides" of the Roman forum. In the word *ambition*, the prefix *ambi-* means "around," and the base *it* means "to go." Even today, an ambitious person is known for being a "go-getter."

Part B:
Combine and Create

Word Relations

Directions: The Latin prefixes *ambi-* and *amphi-* mean "around" or "on both sides." Tell what each of these words has to do with "around" or "on both sides."

1. ambidextrous _____

   _____

2. ambivalent _____

   _____

3. amphitheater_____

   _____

4. ambience_____

   _____

Part C:
Read and Reason

Diary Entry

Directions: Read the following diary entry and answer the questions.

Dear Diary,

Today I learned a new word after gym class. We were asked to play tennis. I have never played tennis before. I started playing with my right hand on the racket, but then I switched to my left and found that both hands did just as well. The teacher called it being ambidextrous. I don't care which hand is my best. I am ambivalent.

Questions:

1. What does it mean to be *ambidextrous*?

_____

_____

2. What is the writer *ambivalent* about?

_____

_____

Part D:

Extend and Explore

Word Analysis

Directions: Look over the words from the "Divide and Conquer" activity on page 19. Then answer the questions.

1. Pick out a word whose meaning you already know. Write the word. What does it mean?

   _____

   _____

2. Pick out a word you find very interesting that you did not know before. Write the word. What does it mean? Why do you find it interesting?

   _____

   _____

3. Pick out a new word you think is very hard. Write the word. What does it mean? Tell why you think it is hard.

   _____

   _____

Part E:
Go for the Gold!

Word Spokes

Directions: Choose a different *ambi-* or *amphi-* word from your cluster for each of the directions below.

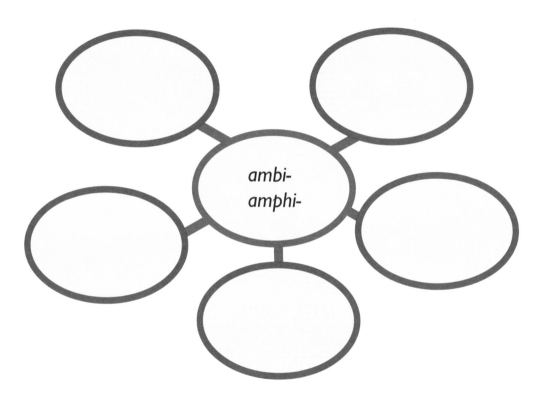

ambi-
amphi-

1. Pick one of the words and write **two synonyms.** _____   _____

2. Pick one of the words and write **two antonyms.** _____   _____

3. Pick one of the words and **write your own definition.** _____

    _____

4. Pick one of the words and **use it in a sentence.** _____

    _____

Part A:
Meet the Root

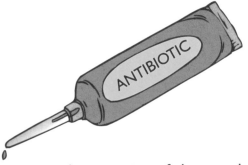

Divide and Conquer

Directions: "Divide" words and then "conquer" them by writing the meaning of the words.

	prefix means	base means	word means
1. contradict	against	*dict* = speak	to speak against a point
2. antipathy		*path* = feeling	
3. counteract		*act* = act	
4. controversy		*vers* = turn	
5. antibiotic		*bi(o)* = life	
6. counterfeit		*feit* = make	
7. contraband		*ban* = decree, prohibit	
8. (to) counter		X	
9. antonym		*onym* = word, name	
10. antiseptic		*sept* = infection	

DID YOU KNOW?

According to the Oxford English Dictionary, *antidisestablishmentarianism* is one of the longest words in the English language. How many of its roots do you recognize? Try to figure out what it means. Then go online to AskOxford where you will find all kinds of interesting word treasures.

Part B:
Combine and Create

Sorting Words

Directions: Sometimes *contra-, contro-, counter-* mean "against" and sometimes
they don't. Put these words on the chart where they belong.

contraband   counterfeit   contrite   contract   contrast
contraption   control   contrary   counterpart   controller
counteract

means "against"	does not mean "against"

Part C:
Read and Reason

Pros and Cons

Directions: Read the following list and answer the questions.

GOING TO SUMMER CAMP

PROS	CONS
Hang out with friends	Miss my friends who are at home
Have time for myself	Have time away from family
Participate in lots of activities and playing	

Questions:

1. What does a pros and cons list do?

   _____

   _____

2. Describe another situation in which you might create a pros and cons list. Give a few examples of each.

   _____

   _____

   _____

Part D:
Extend and Explore

Sentence Writing

Directions: Work with a partner to write sentences that contain both of the following words.

sign/countersign   point/counterpoint   attack/counterattack   pro/con

1. _____

   _____

2. _____

   _____

3. _____

   _____

4. _____

   _____

Part E:
Go for the Gold!

Word Search

Directions: Find the words listed below in the puzzle. Words can be across,
down, on a diagonal, or backwards. Be careful! Some words start
with the same letters.

ANTIBIOTIC   ANTIPATHY   ANTISEPTIC
ANTONYM   CONTRADICT   CONTROVERSY
COUNTER   COUNTERACT   COUNTERFEIT

S	M	G	G	L	P	G	K	Q	F	B	O	W	U	M
Y	I	M	E	G	F	M	N	G	E	G	V	Y	Y	P
A	R	C	C	H	L	S	S	G	N	T	W	N	H	J
N	V	C	O	U	N	T	E	R	E	R	O	K	W	U
T	Q	J	U	N	M	R	G	W	A	T	C	E	E	C
I	L	K	N	W	T	B	T	S	N	J	I	B	U	A
P	A	M	T	L	J	R	C	A	T	N	T	P	M	L
A	U	M	E	C	E	G	A	O	I	N	P	D	B	K
T	S	S	R	F	P	J	R	D	B	A	E	I	D	F
H	L	L	F	V	G	F	E	Z	I	F	S	P	F	D
Y	S	R	E	V	O	R	T	N	O	C	I	I	K	H
O	I	C	I	O	Z	Q	N	T	T	A	T	L	Y	X
M	P	E	T	K	R	F	U	S	I	Q	N	S	E	Y
A	R	I	Z	S	K	Y	O	U	C	M	A	W	J	H
A	K	Q	A	H	J	U	C	W	H	A	Z	Z	A	T

Part A:
Meet the Root

Divide and Conquer

Directions: Your teacher will give you a list of words. "Divide" words into a prefix and a base. Then "conquer" them by writing the meaning of the words.

	word	prefix means	base means	word means
1.				
2.				
3.				
4.				
5.				
6.				
7.				
8.				
9.				
10.				

Part B:
Combine and Create

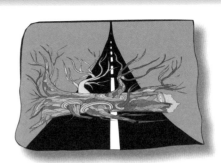

In Search of a Word

Directions: Find a word in each sentence that contains a word part you have studied in this unit. Change the word to its opposite. Then write a sentence with the new word.

1. When we bought our house, my parents and the bank officers countersigned the loan documents.

   Opposite_____

   New sentence_____

   _____

2. I watched the postgame show to see the star of the game.

   Opposite_____

   New sentence_____

   _____

3. The fallen tree obstructed the roadway.

   Opposite_____

   New sentence_____

   _____

4. My teacher said that my answers were too ambiguous to be considered correct.

   Opposite_____

   New sentence_____

   _____

Part C:

Read and Reason

Read the Dialogue

Directions: Read the passage below. Answer the questions.

Because the Greeks and Romans discovered science and medicine, many medical terms are of Greek and Latin origin. These medical words can be very long, but you can often figure out their meaning if you "divide and conquer." These long words often describe common, everyday things. Many people wear braces prescribed by an orthodontist to correct dental malocclusion. At first, the word malocclusion may confuse you because it is so long. But divide it into its Latin parts. It begins with the prefix *mal-*, which means "bad, improper." Then we see the prefix *oc-*, which is assimilated ob-, meaning "up against." The Latin base of this long word is *clus*, which means "close." Dentists created the word malocclusion to describe the "improper" "closing" of the upper teeth "up against" the lower teeth. In everyday language, we might call a malocclusion an overbite or an underbite. Because it might be offensive to some people to be told that they have a bad bite, dentists use this Latin-based word to explain a dental condition that can often be easily corrected. Besides, it sounds more scientific to tell your patients that they have a mild case of malocclusion than it does to tell them they have a "bad bite."

I. Write two short words that explain what *malocclusion* is.

_____   _____

2. *Malocclusion* is made up of three Latin roots. What are they and what do they mean? _____ means _____

_____ means _____

_____ means _____

3. After reading about *malocclusion*, explain what you think an *orthodontist* does.

_____

4. Now check your definition by looking up orthodontist in the dictionary. What do the roots *ortho-* and *dont* mean? Make your definition better by adding or correcting what you wrote.

ortho means _____

dont means _____

Part D:
Extend and Explore

Word Skits

Directions: With one or more partners, choose a word from "Divide and Conquer." Write the word and its definition on an index card. Now work together to create a skit to show the meaning of the word—without talking! Show your skit to others. See if they can guess your word.

Part E:
Go for the Gold!

Sixteen Square Wordo

Directions: Choose a free box and mark it. Then choose words from the list and write one word in each box. Your teacher will give you these words. You can choose the box for each word. Then your teacher will give a clue for each word. Mark an X in the box for each word you match to the clue. If you get four words in a row, column, diagonal, or four corners, call out, "Wordo!"

Part A:
Meet the Root

Divide and Conquer

Directions: "Divide" words and then "conquer" them by writing the meaning of the words. An X means the word does not have a prefix.

	prefix means	base means	word means
1. missile	X	send	a bomb sent in war
2. emit			
3. permit			
4. transmitter			
5. missionary	X		
6. intermittent			
7. promise			
8. submissive			
9. commit			
10. emissions			

DID YOU KNOW?

The ancient Romans loved games and races. They often held horse races in the enormous Colosseum amphitheater. As each race began, Roman men would release their horses and "send" (permitto) them running. Because the horses were permitted to run freely when they left their narrow standing cages, the word *permission* soon came to be associated with allowing things that are normally restricted or forbidden. Even today, we still think of horses when we give people "free rein" to do whatever they want!

Part B:
Combine and Create

Unscrambling Words

Directions: Unscramble the words to fill in the blanks.

The mechanic said our car had two problems. First, the

[1]_____needed to be replaced. We also failed the

[2]_____test because the car exhaust made too much

pollution.

My brother wanted [3]_____to stay up until midnight. My dad

thought he should go to bed at 8 p.m. To solve the problem, they

[4]_____ on 10:30.

Since [5]_____ to our auditorium is limited, we [6]_____

_____ classes slowly before we have assemblies.

[1] A I I M N N O R S S S T

[2] E I I M N O S S S

[3] E I I M N O P R S S

[4] C D E I M M O O P R S

[5] A D I O M N O S S

[6] D I I M S S S

Part C:
Read and Reason

Read the Dialogue

Directions: Read the dialogue below. Answer the questions.

Juan: "Did you watch that new TV show last night? It depicted a secret mission and a submarine's ability to launch missiles."

Steve: "No, I had no idea a new show was on. Is it a drama? A documentary?"

Juan: "It has a kind of missionary zeal as a drama about the ship's captain and his quest to rescue some prisoners of war."

Questions:

1.   What did the new TV show depict?

_____

2.   What is a *mission*? How do you know?

_____

_____

3.   What sort of "*missionary* zeal" does Juan describe, as a focal point for the show?

_____

_____

Part D:
Extend and Explore

Word Chart

Directions: Work with a partner. Use the prefixes to make as many words as possible and put them on the chart.

e-   sub-   per-   dis-   ad-   com-

mit	mission

Now make three sentences with these words. See if you can put more than one word in a sentence. Make sure that your sentences make sense.

1. _____

_____

2. _____

_____

3. _____

_____

Part E:
Go for the Gold!

Word Search

Directions: Find and circle the words in the word search puzzle. Answers can be across, down, on a diagonal, or backwards.

ADMIT	COMPROMISE	DISMISS
INTERMITTENT	NONCOMMITTAL	OMIT
PERMISSION	PERMISSIVE	PERMIT
PREMISE	PROMISE	TRANSMISSION
TRANSMIT	TRANSMITTER	UNREMITTENT

U	P	G	T	T	E	H	A	N	V	A	L	Z	T	Z
N	R	O	I	T	R	G	T	O	S	H	Z	N	W	P
R	E	Y	M	B	M	A	E	I	E	O	E	V	E	R
E	M	G	S	S	E	N	N	S	F	T	B	R	F	P
M	I	N	N	G	G	S	I	S	T	Z	M	J	E	I
I	S	I	A	I	X	M	I	I	M	I	K	R	H	A
T	E	K	R	M	O	Y	M	M	S	I	M	H	W	O
T	T	V	T	R	P	R	O	S	O	I	T	Z	E	B
E	A	I	P	L	E	P	I	N	T	R	I	T	O	V
N	L	E	M	T	H	O	E	A	H	F	P	P	E	B
T	F	V	N	O	N	R	F	R	Y	L	Q	M	F	R
K	D	I	S	M	I	S	S	T	I	M	D	A	O	W
N	O	N	C	O	M	M	I	T	T	A	L	I	T	C
L	B	A	V	W	E	V	I	S	S	I	M	R	E	P
E	V	I	T	O	X	Y	X	I	A	E	Q	F	S	R

Part A:
Meet the Root

Divide and Conquer

Directions: "Divide" words and then "conquer" them by writing the meaning of the words.

	prefix means	base means	word means
1. incredible	not	believe	something that is hard to believe
2. discredit			
3. accredited			

	base means	suffix means	word means
4. credible			
5. creditor			
6. credentials			
7. creed			
8. credence			
9. credulous			
10. credit			

Part B:
Combine and Create

Word Analysis

Directions: *Cred* and *credit* mean "believe." Tell what the words below have to do with "believe."

1. credentials: _____

    _____

2. incredible: _____

    _____

3. discredit: _____

    _____

4. credit: _____

    _____

Part C:
Read and Reason

Read and Answer

Directions: Read the following credit card billing statement and answer the questions.

Ultimate Credit Card Billing Statement
Date: February 19, 2007
Credit Bureau Phone Number: 1-800-543-2143

Last Bill: $250.00 / Paid Two Purchases:
   1. January 27 – Speedy Gas – $24.89
   2. January 30 – Stop Mart – $5.98

                                    Total: $30.87

Next Due Date of Bill: March 15, 2007
Late Payment: March 20, 2007

Questions:

1. What is the purpose of a credit card bill? How do you know?

_____

_____

_____

2. If a person works at a credit card bureau, what do you think they do at work?

_____

_____

_____

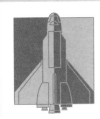

Part D:
Extend and Explore

Making Riddles

Directions: Work with a partner. Make riddles for a few of the words on the list. Then trade riddles with another group. See if they can solve your riddles.

credentials   discredit   credit card   accredited

1. _____
   _____

   Solution: _____

2. _____
   _____

   Solution: _____

3. _____
   _____

   Solution: _____

Word Spokes

Part E:
Go for the Gold!

Directions: Choose a different *cred* or *credit* word from your cluster for each of the directions below.

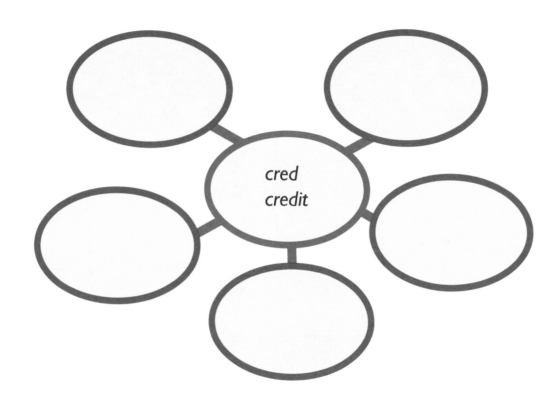

cred
credit

1. Pick one of the words and write **two synonyms.** _____　_____

2. Pick one of the words and write **two antonyms.** _____　_____

3. Pick one of the words and **write your own definition.** _____

_____

4. Pick one of the words and **use it in a sentence.** _____

_____

Part A:
Meet the Root

Divide and Conquer

Directions: "Divide" words and then "conquer" them by writing the meaning of the words.

	prefix means	base means	word means
1. convent			
2. inventor			
3. contravene			
4. intervene			
5. adventure			
6. prevention			
7. event			
8. covenant			
9. reconvene			
10. unconventional			

DID YOU KNOW?

The Roman statesman and general Julius Caesar (100–44 BC) was very proud of his military victories. In the years 47–46 BC, he celebrated four victories over Gaul (modern France), Alexandria (Egypt), Libya (Africa), and Pontus (the part of Asia surrounding the Black Sea). Shortly after these wars, Caesar moved on to Spain, which he also conquered. Caesar celebrated his victories with elaborate parades, called "triumphal processions," that marched through the city of Rome. In one parade, Caesar had 40 elephants with torches in their trunks marching at his side. He also had a huge wagon decorated with three simple Latin words: VENI, VIDI, VICI. What did those simple words mean? "I CAME, I SAW, I CONQUERED." Caesar's boast, "As soon as I came (vini) to a new territory and saw it with my eyes (vidi), I conquered it (vici)," is one of history's most famous sentences.

Part B:
Combine and Create

What Belongs Together?

Directions: Work with a partner. Cross out a word that does not belong with the others. Write your reasons on the line.

prevention   convention   conventional   unconventional

_____

_____

convene   convention   reconvene   intervention

_____

_____

event   convention   inventor   intervention

_____

_____

Part C:
Read and Reason

Newspaper Letter

Directions: Read the following letter from a local newspaper and answer the questions.

Dear Readers,

Regarding the charges that Mayor Miller has stolen city money, our paper would like to state its position. We do not wish to make allegations, and would actually like to contravene the charges until an official court verdict exists. It is our position to regard this statement as a covenant we hold until the Mayor is either convicted or acquitted of these charges.

Questions:

1. What would the newspaper staff like to do about the charges until there is an official court verdict? What does this mean?

   _____

   _____

2. How does the newspaper regard this statement? What does this mean?

   _____

   _____

Part D:
Extend and Explore

Word Skits

Directions: Work with a partner and pick a word. Then write it on an index card. Write what it means and write an example of when you might see it. Tell classmates what root you have used. Then act out the example of when you might see the word. See if your classmates can guess the word.

convention　convene　adventure　invention

Part E:
Go for the Gold!

Sixteen Square Wordo

Directions: Choose a free box and mark it. Then choose words from the list and write one word in each box. Your teacher will give you these words. You can choose the box for each word. Then your teacher will give a clue for each word. Mark an X in the box for each word you match to the clue. If you get four words in a row, column, diagonal, or four corners, call out, "Wordo!"

Part A:
Meet the Root

Divide and Conquer

Directions: "Divide" words and then "conquer" them by writing the meaning of the words. (Hint: Number 10 has two prefixes.)

	prefix means	base means	word means
1. reserve	again	save	to save something for yourself again
2. conserve			
3. servile			
4. preserves			
5. conservation			
6. subservient			
7. reservoir			
8. observatory			
9. servitude			
10. unreserved			

Part B:
Combine and Create

Unscrambling Words

Directions: Unscramble the words to fill in the blanks.

[1]_____ is important for our future. Our family helps

to [2]_____ by recycling and purchasing energy-efficient

appliances.

We called to [3]_____ a table at our favorite restaurant.

Our [4]_____ was for five people at 7:00.

A fiscally [5]_____ person is careful with money. One

way most people do this is to keep some money in [6]_____.

[1] A C E I N N O O R S T V

[2] C E E N O R S V

[3] E E E R R S V

[4] A E E I N O R R S T V

[5] A C E E I N O R S T V V

[6] E E E R R S V

Journal

Part C:
Read and Reason

Directions: Read the following journal entry and answer the questions.

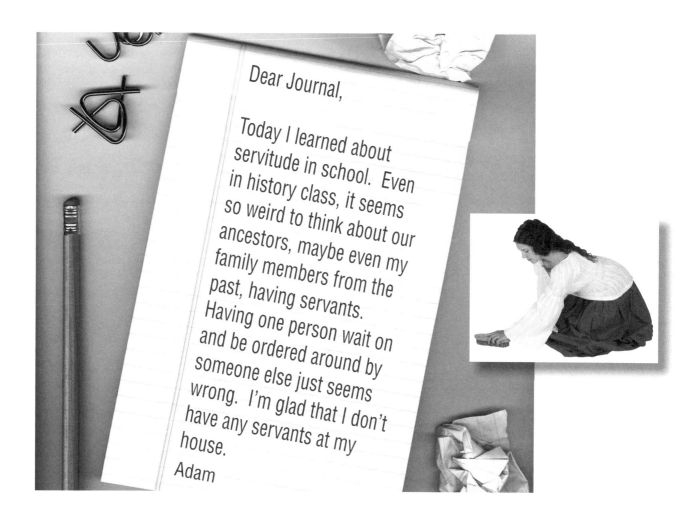

Dear Journal,

Today I learned about servitude in school. Even in history class, it seems so weird to think about our ancestors, maybe even my family members from the past, having servants. Having one person wait on and be ordered around by someone else just seems wrong. I'm glad that I don't have any servants at my house.

Adam

Questions:

1.   Define *servitude*.

   _____

   _____

2.   Explain the role of a *servant* as Adam describes it in his journal.

   _____

Part D:
Extend and Explore

Making Words

Directions: Work with a partner to make as many *serv, servat* words as possible with these prefixes. Make sure the words have something to do with "save," "keep," or "serve."

ob-			
re-			
pre-			
con-			

DID YOU KNOW?

When European settlers came to North America, they drove the native people off their land. American history tells of many battles between the early European pioneers and the Native American tribes. By the end of the nineteenth century, most of these tribes had been forced to give up almost all their land. In order to *preserve* their way of life, however, Native Americans asked to "keep" "back" certain portions for themselves. These areas where they could live together in peace came to be known as *reservations*.

Part E:
Go for the Gold!

Crossword Puzzle

Directions: Read the clues below. Fill in the crossword puzzle with the correct words.

Across
2. in olden times a person who was like a slave, lived on land, and worked the land
5. serving someone from below
8. to set food before
9. a person hired or kept to do certain duties
11. to keep together; to keep things the same
13. not held back or set aside for

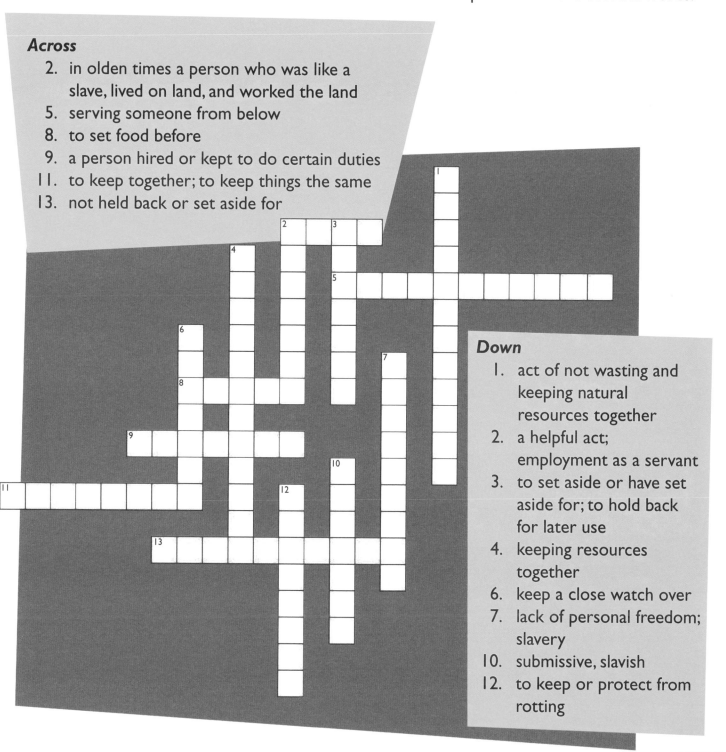

Down
1. act of not wasting and keeping natural resources together
2. a helpful act; employment as a servant
3. to set aside or have set aside for; to hold back for later use
4. keeping resources together
6. keep a close watch over
7. lack of personal freedom; slavery
10. submissive, slavish
12. to keep or protect from rotting

Part A:
Meet the Root

Divide and Conquer

Directions: "Divide" words and then "conquer" them by writing the meaning of the words. An x means the word does not have a prefix.

	prefix means	base means	word means
1. propeller	through	push	to push through air and keep a plane in the air
2. appeal			
3. repellent			
4. expelled			
5. pulse	X		
6. repulsive			
7. impulsive			
8. compulsive			
9. pulsating	X		
10. expulsion			

DID YOU KNOW?

The prefix *com-* usually means "with" or "together," but with some bases it can mean "very." When *com-* attaches to *pel-* or *pul-*, it refers to behaviors that are "very" "driven." Many people feel *compelled* or "very" "driven" to play sports. A *compulsive* shopper feels "very" "driven" to shop all the time. And from time to time, some of us have a *compulsion* for chocolate: we just feel "very" "driven" to eat it!

Part B:
Combine and Create

Word Chart

Directions: Sometimes *pel* means "drive" or "push," and sometimes it doesn't. Put these words on the chart where they belong.

pelican   repel   pelt   propeller   pelvis   expel   compel   pellet

means to "drive" or "push"	does not mean to "drive" or "push"

DID YOU KNOW?

The U.S. court system has three levels. The district courts are the lowest level. Next is the district Court of Appeals, which hears cases when the verdict from a district court is in dispute. In a Court of Appeals, appellants try to reverse a verdict by "driving" it "to" a higher court. The judge in a Court of Appeals must decide whether or not the first judgment was fair. If they are still not satisfied, appellants can ask the U.S. Supreme Court to hear the case. Known as the "last court of appeal," the Supreme Court is the highest court in the country. It has the power to overrule the decisions of all other courts.

Part C:
Read and Reason

Dialogue

Directions: Read the following short dialogue and answer the questions.

Juan: "Can you feel my pulse?"

Marie: "Yeah. It's going really fast. Were you just exercising?"

Juan: "I've got a pulsating rhythm from running around the block as fast as I can. Kind of like the beat to that new song on the radio."

Questions:

1. What is a *pulse?* _____

_____

2. Why would Juan compare his *pulse* to a song on the radio? _____

_____

Part D:
Extend and Explore

Word Matrix

Directions: Work with a partner to complete the matrix. Some boxes may be blank.

	pel	*pulsive*	*pulsion*
re-			
ex-			
com-			
pro-			

Part E:
Go for the Gold!

Word Spokes

Directions: Choose a different *pel*, *puls*, or *peal* word from your cluster for each of the directions below.

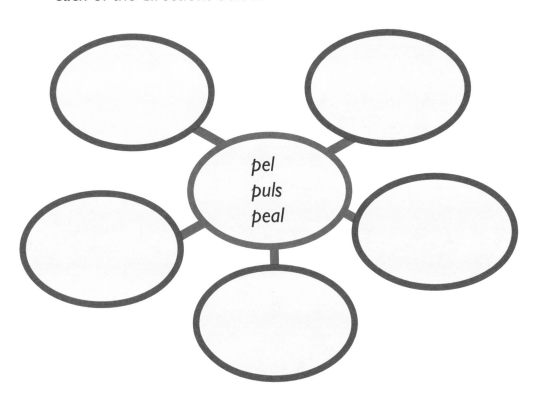

pel
puls
peal

1. Pick one of the words and write **two synonyms.** _____ _____

2. Pick one of the words and write **two antonyms.** _____ _____

3. Pick one of the words and **write your own definition.** _____

   _____

4. Pick one of the words and **use it in a sentence.** _____

   _____

Part A:
Meet the Root

Divide and Conquer

Directions: Your teacher will give you a list of words. "Divide" words into a prefix and a base. Then "conquer" them by writing the meaning of the words.

	word	prefix means	base means	word means
1.				
2.				
3.				
4.				
5.				
6.				
7.				
8.				
9.				
10.				

Part B:
Combine and Create

Word Analysis

Directions: Look over the words from the "Divide and Conquer" activities in this unit. Then answer the questions.

1. Pick out a word whose meaning you already know. Write the word. What does it mean?

   _____

   _____

2. Pick out a word you find very interesting that you did not know before. Write the word. What does it mean? Why do you find it interesting?

   _____

   _____

   _____

3. Pick out a new word you think is very hard. Write the word. What does it mean? Tell why you think it is hard.

   _____

   _____

   _____

Part C:
Read and Reason

Show What You Know

Directions: Read the passage and answer the questions.

The ancient Greeks invented the outdoor theater by building seats into a natural hillside. Because the hillsides were so large, an outdoor Greek theater could easily hold over 15,000 spectators. The word theater comes from the Greek word meaning "to watch, to gaze." The theater was the place to see things!

The Romans, by contrast, built their theaters as indoor structures inside the city. Roman theaters had walls around them and were therefore much smaller than the Greek outdoor theaters. But in the year 80 AD, the Romans built their first truly huge theater under the leadership of emperors from the Flavian family. The Flavian Amphitheater was so big and colossal in size that it came to be called the Colosseum.

Instead of having all the seats face in one direction toward the stage, the Colosseum was the first true amphitheater ("theater in the round") because it was built in the shape of a huge oval with seats all around the center. The Romans boasted that they were now more advanced builders than the ancient Greeks because their amphitheater could hold 50,000 people. The Colosseum still stands today and remains one of the largest tourist attractions in Rome.

Questions:

1. What do you think is the most interesting information in this passage?
   Explain why. _____

   _____

2. Do the Romans seem to be more *ambitious* builders than the Greeks?
   Explain why you think so. _____

   _____

3. The Romans loved to watch gladiators fight each other in the Colosseum. They especially liked watching one gladiator kill another. Do you feel any *ambivalence* about this bloody entertainment? Why? _____

   _____

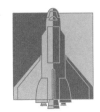

Part D:
Extend and Explore

Word Skits

Directions: Work with a partner and pick a word. Then write it on an index card. Write what it means and write an example of when you might see it. Tell classmates what root you have used. Then act out the example of when you might see the word. See if your classmates can guess the word.

convention   convene   adventure   invention

Part E:
Go for the Gold!

Crossword Puzzle

Directions: Read the clues below. Fill in the crossword puzzle with the correct words.

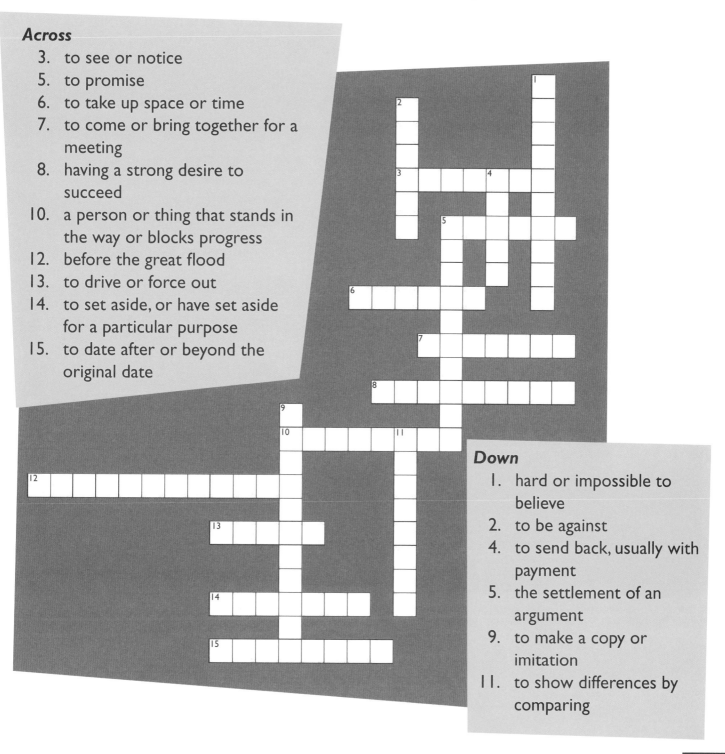

Across

3. to see or notice
5. to promise
6. to take up space or time
7. to come or bring together for a meeting
8. having a strong desire to succeed
10. a person or thing that stands in the way or blocks progress
12. before the great flood
13. to drive or force out
14. to set aside, or have set aside for a particular purpose
15. to date after or beyond the original date

Down

1. hard or impossible to believe
2. to be against
4. to send back, usually with payment
5. the settlement of an argument
9. to make a copy or imitation
11. to show differences by comparing

Part A:
Meet the Root

Divide and Conquer

Directions: "Divide" words and then "conquer" them by writing the meaning of the words. (Hint: Number 10 has two prefixes.) An X means the word does not have a prefix.

	prefix means	base means	word means
1. convertible	with	change	a car that can be changed by lowering the roof
2. reverse			
3. vertical	X		
4. controversial			
5. versatile	X		
6. advertisemet			
7. conversation			
8. diverse			
9. conversion			
10. irreversible			

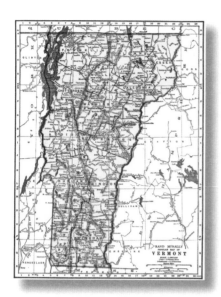

Part B:
Combine and Create

Word Chart

Directions: Sometimes *ver* means "turn" or "change," and sometimes it doesn't. Put these words on the chart where they belong. Use a dictionary if necessary.

vertical	verse	verify	versatile	vertebra
vertigo	convertible	Vermont	version	vermin
reverse	diversity	inverse		

means "turn or change"	doesn't mean "turn or change"

Part C:
Read and Reason

News Report

Directions: Read the following news report and answer the questions.

Wanted! Verses of Poetry!

Either Free Verse (Unrhymed) or Rhyming Verse Accepted

We need versatile styles of poetry for our next issue of Poetry Lessonly, a nonprofit and free magazine that publishes today's youngest school writers. To submit your verse(s) of poetry, please note the information below:

Due date: March 12, 2007 @ 7 P.M.

Mail To: Dr. Poetry Mix

1111 Smithville Street

Rhyme City,

FL 67890

Questions:

1. What is the poetry contest looking for? How do you know?

_____

_____

2. What does it mean to be *versatile*? _____

_____

_____

Part D:
Extend and Explore

Word Matrix

Directions: Work with a partner to complete the matrix. Some boxes may have more than one word. Others may be blank.

	vert	vers	version
con-			
sub-			
in-			
re-			
di-			

Part E:
Go for the Gold!

Word Spokes

Directions: Choose a different *vert, vers* word from your cluster for each of the directions below.

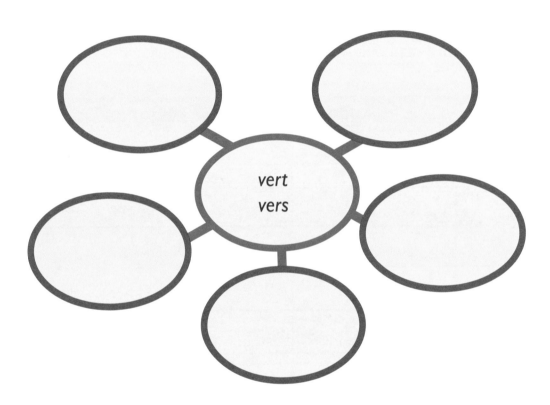

1. Pick one of the words and write **two synonyms.** _____ _____

2. Pick one of the words and write **two antonyms.** _____ _____

3. Pick one of the words and **write your own definition.**_____

    _____

4. Pick one of the words and **use it in a sentence.** _____

    _____

Part A:
Meet the Root

Divide and Conquer

Directions: "Divide" words and then "conquer" them by writing the meaning of the words. (Hint: Numbers 9 and 10 have two prefixes.) An X means the word does not have a prefix.

	prefix means	base means	word means
1. contents	together	hold	items held together in something
2. retain	_____	_____	_____
3. tenacious	X	_____	_____
4. detention	_____	_____	_____
5. tenure	X	_____	_____
6. continent	_____	_____	_____
7. detain	_____	_____	_____
8. abstain	_____	_____	_____
9. discontinue	___ ___	_____	_____
10. discontent	___ ___	_____	_____

Part B:
Combine and Create

Unscrambling Words

Directions: Unscramble the words to fill in the blanks.

One girl in our class was so [1]_____ to our teacher that

she was given a [2]_____.

It was very hard to [3]_____ the book I wanted. I even called

the publisher, who said that publication had been [4]_____.

We know that it's important to [5]_____ our car by

taking it to a mechanic every now and then. In fact, my parents have "car

[6]_____" in our family budget.

[1] E E I I M N N P R T T

[2] D E E I N N O T T

[3] A B I N O T

[4] C D D E I I N N O S T U

[5] A A I I M N N T

[6] A A C E E I M N N N T

Part C:
Read and Reason

Advice Column

Directions: Read the following advice column and answer the questions.

Dear Adelia Advice,

I am a tenacious and excitable new professor at a small college. I recently accepted this position on the tenet that I would earn tenure after five to six years at the university. How should I go about preparing for tenure?

Patty Professor

Dear Patty Professor,
To earn tenure you must abide by and support the basic beliefs— or tenets—of the university. My advice is to find out what these guiding beliefs are and stand by them.

Adelia Advice

Questions:

1. What is Adelia Advice's recommendation about *tenure*? How does this help you understand the meaning of *tenure*? _____

_____

2. What kind of professor is Patty Professor? What does this mean? _____

_____

Part D:
Extend and Explore

Making Riddles

Directions: Work with a partner. Make riddles for a few of the words on the list. Then trade riddles with another group. See if they can solve your riddles.

detention   continent   container   continue   obtain   sustain

1. _____

   _____

   Solution: _____

2. _____

   _____

   Solution: _____

3. _____

   _____

   Solution: _____

Part E:
Go for the Gold!

Word Search

Directions: Find and circle the words in the word search puzzle. Answers can be across, down, diagonal, or backwards.

CONTAIN	CONTINENT	CONTINUE
CONTINUUM	RETAIN	RETAINER
RETENTION	RETENTIVE	SUSTAIN
TENABLE	TENACIOUS	TENACITY
TENET	TENURE	UNTENABLE

N	B	R	F	M	S	R	C	F	U	T	I	I	D	U
O	P	E	H	Y	E	U	B	C	N	N	N	E	J	N
I	P	B	U	T	Y	O	S	E	F	P	F	L	X	T
T	O	O	A	N	D	G	N	T	O	J	X	B	C	E
N	V	I	R	E	I	I	Y	Q	A	O	B	A	T	N
E	N	M	O	I	T	T	T	C	Y	I	S	N	T	A
T	V	C	O	N	T	I	N	U	U	M	N	E	H	B
E	B	I	O	U	M	H	M	O	Z	R	N	T	W	L
R	L	C	T	E	S	U	O	I	C	A	N	E	T	E
M	S	Q	N	N	X	B	A	S	C	T	E	N	E	T
U	J	H	N	Z	E	S	M	I	X	E	B	I	K	V
H	T	A	Q	K	C	T	T	C	O	N	T	A	I	N
A	W	F	J	J	M	Y	E	L	R	U	W	B	Z	P
R	E	N	I	A	T	E	R	R	V	R	G	J	U	J
P	O	Q	P	Q	Q	H	V	J	K	E	O	Q	H	P

Part A:
Meet the Root

Divide and Conquer

Directions: "Divide" words and then "conquer" them by writing the meaning of the words. (Hint: Numbers 9 and 10 have two prefixes.) An X means the word does not have a prefix.

	prefix means	base means	word means
1. perfect	_____	_____	_____
2. defect	_____	_____	_____
3. factory	X	_____	_____
4. deficient	_____	_____	_____
5. faculty	X	_____	_____
6. confection	_____	_____	_____
7. affection	_____	_____	_____
8. effective	_____	_____	_____
9. imperfect	_____	_____	_____
10. disinfect	_____	_____	_____

DID YOU KNOW?

The word *facile*, which means "done with ease," is quite versatile. A person who "does" something smoothly and gracefully is a *facile* performer. Even though a *facile* guitarist and a *facile* ice skater make their jobs look "easy," they "do" something beautiful that takes years of special training. Such skilled artists do their work with great *facility*. The plural word *facilities* refers to conditions that make a job or task "easier." A good office provides excellent working *facilities*.

Part B:
Combine and Create

Word Chart

Directions: Sometimes *fac* means "do" or "make," and sometimes it doesn't. Put these words on the chart where they belong.

fact	factory	facial	facing	factual
facility	facet	facetious	faction	faculty

means "do or make"	does not mean "do or make"

Part C:
Read and Reason

Newspaper Story

Directions: Read the following newspaper story and answer the questions.

Factory Thief Strikes Again!
Tuesday, April 3, 2007:

In today's news, a clothing factory thief has struck again. This time, he has stolen 35 rolls of fabric for next year's spring line from the clothing facility. "It is now proven fact," said Chief of Police Mayer, "that this is the same thief who broke into the factory last year." The thief left his fingerprints all over as evidence, both this year and last year.

Questions:

1. What kind of *factory* does the article talk about? What happens inside of a factory?

   _____

   _____

2. What *facts* emerge from the story? Who states these facts?

   _____

   _____

Part D:
Extend and Explore

Word Skits

Directions:　Work with a partner and pick a word. Then write it on an index card. Write what it means and write an example of when you might see it. Tell classmates what root you have used. Then act out the example of when you might see the word. See if your classmates can guess the word.

facility　　factory　　perfection　　infection　　perfect

Part E:
Go for the Gold!

Sixteen Square Wordo

Directions: Choose a free box and mark it. Then choose words from the list and write one word in each box. Your teacher will give you these words. You can choose the box for each word. Then your teacher will give a clue for each word. Mark an X in the box for each word you match to the clue. If you get four words in a row, column, diagonal, or four corners, call out, "Wordo!"

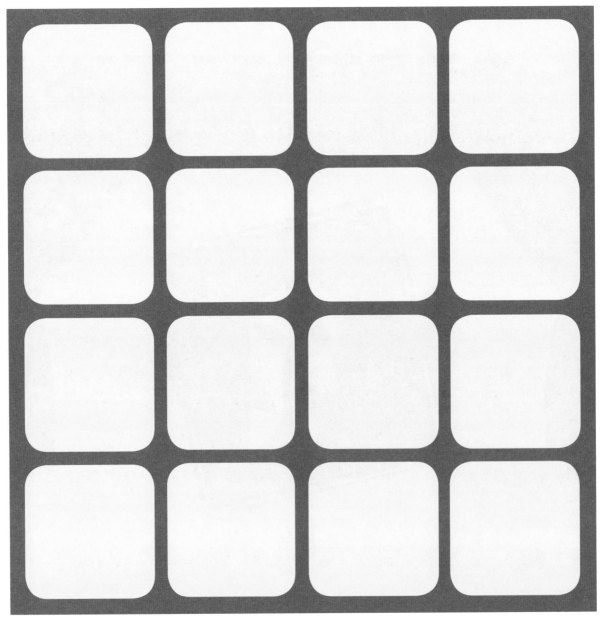

Part A:
Meet the Root

Divide and Conquer

Directions: "Divide" words and then "conquer" them by writing the meaning of the words. (Hint: Numbers 9 and 10 have two prefixes.) An X means the word does not have a prefix.

	prefix means	base means	word means
1. expenses	_____	_____	_____
2. depend	_____	_____	_____
3. pendant	X	_____	_____
4. appendix	_____	_____	_____
5. pendulum	X	_____	_____
6. suspenseful	_____	_____	_____
7. dispenser	_____	_____	_____
8. compensate	_____	_____	_____
9. indispensable	_____ _____	_____	_____
10. independent	_____ _____	_____	_____

DID YOU KNOW?

Suspend, suspenders, and *suspense* all share the prefix *sus-* and the base *pend*. But what meaning do these words have in common? *Sus-* (assimilated *sub-*) means "under" and *pend* means "hang." A high-wire artist is *literally suspended* in air, hanging "under" a trapeze. *Suspenders* literally hold up pants, which "hang" "under" a shirt. But a *suspense* story leaves us *figuratively suspended*. In fact, *suspenseful* stories are often called "cliff hangers" because they "leave us hanging" with curiosity about what will happen next!

Part B:
Combine and Create

Word Analysis

Directions: *Pend* and *pens* mean "weigh," "hang," or "pay." Tell what these words have to do with weighing, hanging, or paying.

1. pendulum: _____

   _____

2. expend: _____

   _____

3. compensate: _____

   _____

4. pension: _____

   _____

   _____

Part C:
Read and Reason

Dialogue

Directions: Read the dialogue below. Answer the questions.

Jorge: "My teacher said that watching my grades go up and down is like watching a pendulum swing back and forth."

Heidi: "What does that mean?"

Jorge: "A pendulum swings back and forth, spending equal time in both places rather than in one place only."

Heidi: "So she means that your grades aren't consistent?"

Jorge: "Yep."

Questions:

1.   How does Jorge describe a *pendulum*?

   _____

2.   What does it do? Can you think of something else that works like a *pendulum*?

   _____

   _____

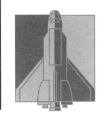

Part D:
Extend and Explore

Word Matrix

Directions: Work with a partner to complete the matrix. The word part *pen* will need to be added. You may need to add another syllable or two to make a word. Some boxes may be empty.

	-sive	-ent	-ion
de-			
ex-			
co-			
com-			
dis-			

Part E:
Go for the Gold!

Crossword Puzzle

Directions: Read the clues below. Fill in the crossword puzzle with the correct words.

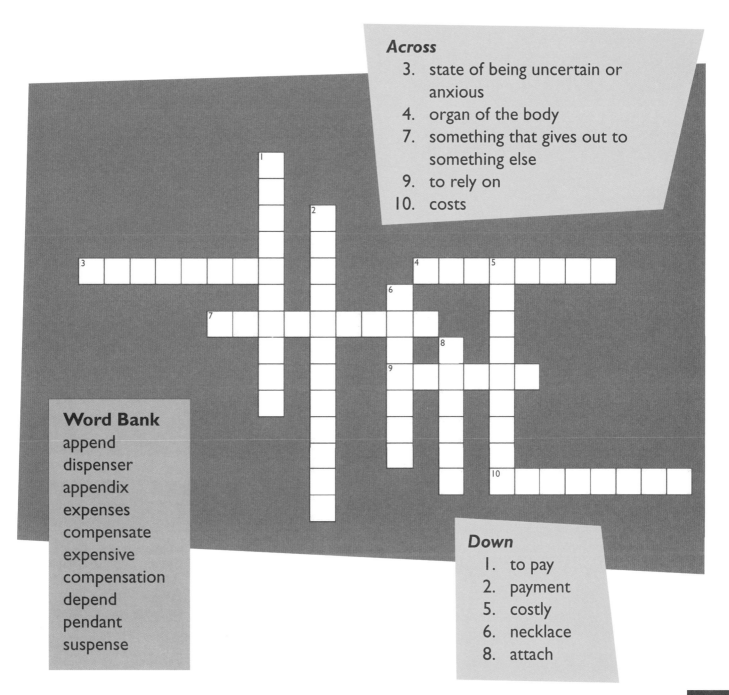

Across

3. state of being uncertain or anxious
4. organ of the body
7. something that gives out to something else
9. to rely on
10. costs

Word Bank

append
dispenser
appendix
expenses
compensate
expensive
compensation
depend
pendant
suspense

Down

1. to pay
2. payment
5. costly
6. necklace
8. attach

Part A:
Meet the Root

Divide and Conquer

Directions: "Divide" words and then "conquer" them by writing the meaning of the words. An X means the word does not have a prefix.

	prefix means	base means	word means
1. consent	_____	_____	_____
2. dissent	_____	_____	_____
3. sensational	X	_____	_____
4. nonsensical	_____	_____	_____
5. sentimental	X	_____	_____
6. presentiment	_____	_____	_____
7. sensor	X	_____	_____
8. resent	_____	_____	_____
9. insensitive	_____	_____	_____
10. sensible	X	_____	_____

DID YOU KNOW?

Scientists say that each of us has five senses—or ways of feeling—that help us understand the world, but the senses of *sight, sound, taste, smell,* and *touch* can describe both feeling and thinking. When we use our "*sense* of touch," we are "feeling," but when we hear someone "making good *sense*" as they talk, we are "thinking" about the thoughts they are communicating. And, of course, whenever we hear, touch, see, taste, or smell anything exceptional, we find it *sensational!*

Part B:
Combine and Create

Unscrambling Words

Directions: Unscramble the words to fill in the blanks.

My sister is [1]_____ to insect stings, so she see an allergist

who is working to [2]_____ her.

Our family is very [3]_____ about birthdays. We have family

traditions that are [4]_____. Everyone enjoys them!

Instead of voting "yes" and "no" about whether to play baseball at recess, our

teacher asked how many of us [5]_____ and how many

[6]_____.

[1] E E I I N S S T V

[2] D E E E I N S S T Z

[3] A E E I L M N N S T T

[4] A A E I L N N O S S T

[5] A D E E N S S T

[6] D D E E I N S S T

Part C:
Read and Reason

Student Note

Directions: Read the following note from one student to another (during their health class) and answer the questions.

Amy,

Mrs. Miller is talking so much about our senses that she is making me hungry for lunch. I'm so sensitive around this time of day, right before I eat, that any mention of sensations gets me craving some pizza or something. How about you?

James

Questions:

1. What *sense* is James describing above? How do you know?

   _____

2. What does it mean to be *sensitive*?

   _____

Part D:
Extend and Explore

Making Riddles

Directions: Here are several words. Work with a partner to develop riddles for two of them. Then give your riddles to another group of students. See if they can figure them out.

sensitive　　sensible　　sentimental　　resentment

1. _____

_____

Solution: _____

2. _____

_____

Solution: _____

Part E:
Go for the Gold!

Word Spokes

Directions: Choose a different *sent, sens* word from your cluster for each of these directions. You will use all five of the words you chose when you have finished!

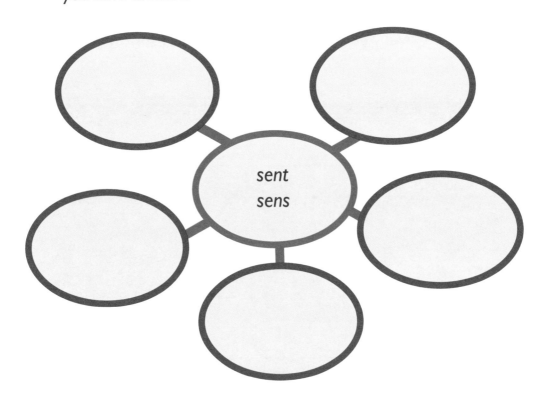

1. Pick one of the words and write **two synonyms.** _____   _____

2. Pick one of the words and write **two antonyms.** _____   _____

3. Pick one of the words and **write your own definition.** _____

    _____

4. Pick one of the words and **use it in a sentence.** _____

    _____

Part A:
Meet the Root

Divide and Conquer

Directions: Your teacher will give you a list of words. "Divide" words into a prefix and a base. Then "conquer" them by writing the meaning of the words.

	word	prefix means	base means	word means
1.	_____	_____	_____	_____
2.	_____	_____	_____	_____
3.	_____	_____	_____	_____
4.	_____	_____	_____	_____
5.	_____	_____	_____	_____
6.	_____	_____	_____	_____
7.	_____	_____	_____	_____
8.	_____	_____	_____	_____
9.	_____	_____	_____	_____
10.	_____	_____	_____	_____

Part B:
Combine and Create

Word Analysis

Directions: Look over the words from the "Divide and Conquer" activities in this unit. Then answer the questions.

1. Pick out a word whose meaning you already know. Write the word. What does it mean?

   _____

   _____

2. Pick out a word you find very interesting that you did not know before. Write the word. What does it mean? Why do you find it interesting?

   _____

   _____

3. Pick out a new word you think is very hard. Write the word. What does it mean? Tell why you think it is hard.

   _____

   _____

Part C:
Read and Reason

Reading Passage

Directions: Read the passage and answer the questions.

Have you ever wondered why poetry is written in *verses?* We owe it to the ancient Romans, who thought that writing poetry was similar to farming. When a farmer plowed, he walked behind his horse or mule, guiding the animal to cut a straight line, called a furrow, in the soil. As they reached the end of the field, the farmer simply *turned* around and continued to plow the next row. When he reached the end of that furrow, the farmer turned around again, going back and forth until he finished the entire plot. In this way, the furrows of his plowed field were all neat, straight, and even. When a Roman poet set out to write verses, he saw himself plowing the page with his pen or stylus (a kind of writing tool). Like a farmer plowing neat and even rows for planting, the poet wrote in neat and even lines, "turning" at the end of one line of poetry and then moving on to the next. This is why we say that poets write in verses. Today, we still call the art of writing poetry *versification.* Do you recall a book of poems by Robert Louis Stevenson (1850–1894) called *A Child's Garden of Verses?* In calling his poems a "garden," Stevenson reminds us of the connection between "turning" soil in a garden and "turning" a beautiful line of *verse.* And when we compliment someone on a pleasing "turn of phrase," we are really comparing their expression to the *verses* of a Roman poet!

Questions:

1. In your own words, explain how the Romans thought that "plowing" and "poetry" were similar. _____

   _____

2. What is *versification?* _____

   convert-revert divert-subvert reverse-inverse adverse-converse

3. Try your hand at "turning a phrase" by writing a four-line verse that uses at least one of the word pairs above: _____

   _____

   _____

   _____

Part D:
Extend and Explore

Word Skits

Directions: With one or more partners, choose a word from "Divide and Conquer." Write the word and its definition on an index card. Now work together to create a skit to show the meaning of the word—without talking! Show your skit to others. See if they can guess your word.

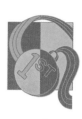

Part E:
Go for the Gold!

Sixteen Square Wordo

Directions: Choose a free box and mark it. Then choose words from the list and write one word in each box. Your teacher will give you these words. You can choose the box for each word. Then your teacher will give a clue for each word. Mark an X in the box for each word you match to the clue. If you get four words in a row, column, diagonal, or four corners, call out, "Wordo!"

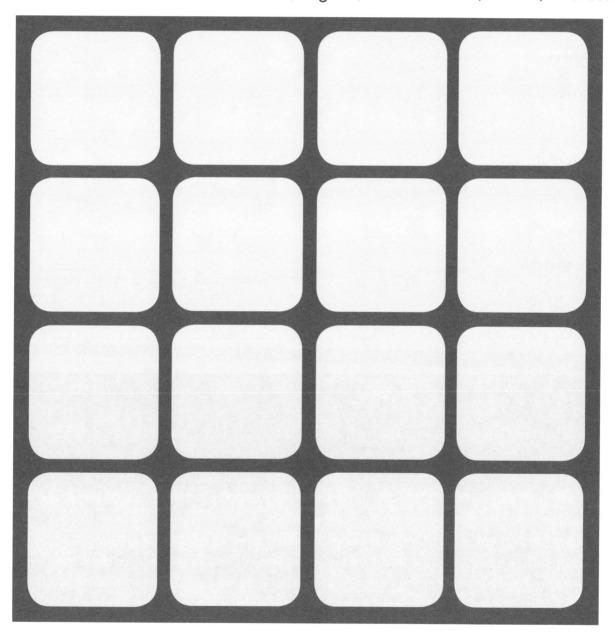

Part A:

Meet the Root

Divide and Conquer

Directions: "Divide" words and then "conquer" them by writing the meaning of the words. (Note: Number 9 is base + base and number 10 is base + suffix.)

	prefix means	base means	word means
1. revive	_____	_____	_____
2. survivor	_____	_____	_____
3. vivacious	X	_____	_____
4. vivid	X	_____	_____
5. amphibian	_____	_____	_____
6. antibiotics	*anti-* = against	_____	_____
7. vital	X	_____	_____
8. convivial	_____	_____	_____
9. biography	_____	_____	_____
10. biology	_____	_____	_____

DID YOU KNOW?

When two organisms depend on each other to stay alive, we say they are living in *symbiosis*. The word symbiosis comes from two Greek roots: *sym-* (together) and *bi(o)-* (life, live). The rhinoceros is *symbiotic* with a bird named the "oxpecker." Sometimes called a "tick bird," the little bird rides happily on the back of this huge animal, keeping it alive by eating ticks off its hide. Since ticks are the only food these birds can eat, the rhinoceros keeps the bird alive as well. In a *symbiotic* relationship, one organism cannot live without the other. In fact, if one dies, the other one does too. By taking care of each other's needs, then, the rhinoceros and the tick bird live in a *symbiotic* relationship that enables their mutual *survival*.

Part B:
Combine and Create

Word Association

Directions: *Vit, viv, and bi(o)* relate to life or living. Write what these words have to do with life or living.

vitality _____

vitamins _____

biography _____

biology _____

DID YOU KNOW?

The ancient Romans loved to devote long hours to banquets. Their dinner parties could begin in the early morning and last into the late hours of the night! As they feasted on delicacies, they talked to one another, recited poetry, and shared stories from Greek and Roman mythology. The more they ate and drank, the more festive they became. The Romans felt truly "alive" at parties when they were "with" their friends and relatives enjoying each other's company. Indeed, the dinner party was the time and place to share life with others. For this reason, the Romans called their banquets *convivia* or occasions filled "very" much "with life." Today, we still say that time spent with friends puts us in a *convivial* mood.

Part C:
Read and Reason

Advertisement

Directions: Read the following advertisement and answer the questions.

Vital Vitamins!

These vitamins will vitalize your organs to an all new level—making them all work together for a stronger, healthier, and more active body metabolism. The results are vivid!

Questions:

1. Why are these vitamins *vital*? What does it mean to *vitalize* your bodily organs?

   _____

2. Why would the advertisers say the results are *vivid*?

   _____

Part D:
Extend and Explore

Word Skits

Directions: With one or more partners, choose a word from "Divide and Conquer." Write the word and its definition on an index card. Now work together to create a skit to show the meaning of the word—without talking! Show your skit to others. See if they can guess your word.

Part E:
Go for the Gold!

Word Search

Directions: Find and circle the words in the word search puzzle. Answers can be across, down, diagonal, or backwards.

AMPHIBIAN   ANTIBIOTICS   AUTOBIOGRAPHY
BIOCHEMISTRY   BIOGRAPHY   BIOENGINEERING
BIOETHICS   BIOLOGICAL   BIOMEDICINE
BIOPSY   BIOSPHERE   SIGNS
VIANDS   VITAL   VITALIZE
VIVACIOUS   VIVACITY   VIVIAN
VIVID

B	B	E	G	E	Y	S	P	O	I	B	B	E	N	T
R	I	I	N	J	R	K	N	A	O	I	V	V	I	L
E	A	O	O	I	R	E	K	O	O	W	I	I	I	A
V	M	T	E	L	C	V	H	D	I	V	E	V	T	U
I	P	L	E	N	O	I	E	P	A	T	I	E	R	T
T	H	S	A	H	G	G	D	C	S	V	P	R	E	O
A	I	D	W	T	R	I	I	E	A	O	D	O	S	B
L	B	N	B	A	I	O	N	C	M	B	I	T	Q	I
I	I	A	D	A	U	V	I	E	A	O	V	B	V	O
Z	A	I	D	S	J	T	N	M	E	L	I	M	I	G
E	N	V	G	U	Y	G	I	O	M	R	V	B	T	R
G	Y	R	T	S	I	M	E	H	C	O	I	B	A	A
A	N	T	I	B	I	O	T	I	C	S	A	N	U	P
A	Y	H	P	A	R	G	O	I	B	R	N	D	G	H
Z	B	I	O	E	T	H	I	C	S	N	G	I	S	Y

Part A:
Meet the Root

Divide and Conquer

Directions: "Divide" words and then "conquer" them by writing the meaning of the words. An X means the word does not have a prefix.

	prefix means	base means	word means
1. prenatal	before	give birth	the time before giving birth
2. postnatal			
3. natural	X		
4. genetics	X		
5. congenital			
6. cognates			
7. natives	X		
8. regenerate			
9. degenerate			
10. innate			

DID YOU KNOW?

In the fifth century AD, barbarians destroyed the city of Rome. For nearly a thousand years, Europe entered a period of little culture known as the Dark Ages. Happily, in the fourteenth century, Europe rediscovered the lost learning of Greece and Rome. Scientists, painters, and sculptors, like Galileo, Michelangelo, and Leonardo da Vinci, turned to the ancients to inspire their own creative *genius*. This shining period in European culture is now called the *Renaissance* or "re" "birth." Because *Renaissance* is a French word, its Latin roots are disguised. But if you look closely, you will see that *nais* comes from the base *nat* (born) and the prefix *re-* (again).

Part B:
Combine and Create

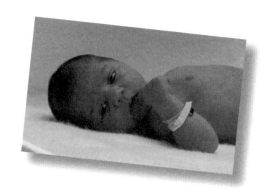

Word Chart

Directions: Sometimes *gen, gener,* and *nat, natur* mean "to produce" or are
related to birth, and sometimes they are not. Put these words
on the chart where they belong. Use a dictionary if necessary.

natal   nature   natty   regency   genius
generally   generous   genie   gentle   genetics
congenial   congenital   gender   natatorium

means to birth/produce	does not mean to birth/ produce

A Conversation

Part C:
Read and Reason

Directions: Read the following conversation between a teacher and a student and answer the questions.

Teacher: "The Native Americans have had a long, rich history in the United States. Their customs and traditions are worthy of our attention every day, and in this next unit we will learn about the Native American nation and its national beliefs."

Natalie: "Do they have a national anthem like ours?"

Teacher: "They have many native songs that Mrs. Koklo, the music teacher, is preparing to teach you."

Questions:

1. What will the students be studying?

   _____

2. What kind of information does the teacher specifically mention?

   _____

3. What is a *national* anthem?

   _____

4. Will the students learn the Native American *national* anthem?

   _____

Part D:
Extend and Explore

Sentence Starters

Directions: Work with a partner to complete these sentences by selecting a word from the list. Try to put a clue about the word's meaning in your sentences. You and your partner are a team. Together choose one of the sentences to read out loud, but skip over the word. See if your classmates can guess the missing word.

native	naturalized	citizens	natural
genetics	generation	ungenerous	innate
generous	genius		

1. While I was trying to _____

_____

2. How do you know if _____

_____

3. Where in the world can _____

_____

4. What would you think about _____

_____

5. Why should _____

_____

Part E:
Go for the Gold!

Sixteen Square Wordo

Directions: Choose a free box and mark it. Then choose words from the list and write one word in each box. Your teacher will give you these words. You can choose the box for each word. Then your teacher will give a clue for each word. Mark an X in the box for each word you match to the clue. If you get four words in a row, column, diagonal, or four corners, call out, "Wordo!"

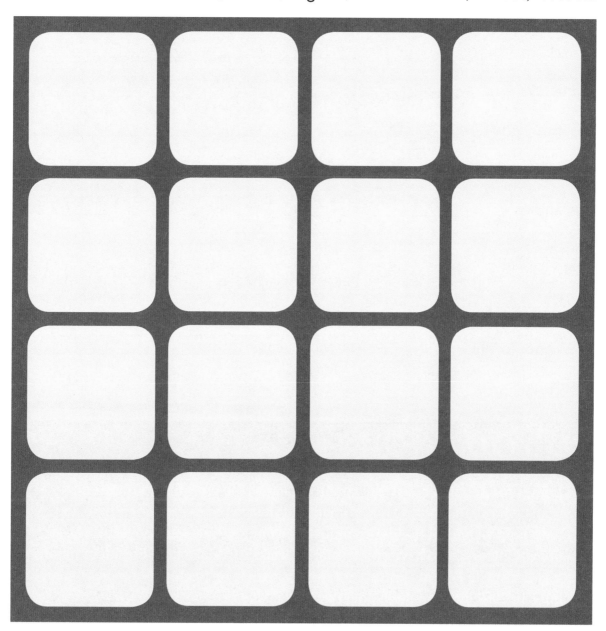

Latin Base *human* and Greek Base *anthrop(o)* = "human being, humankind"

Part A:
Meet the Root

Divide and Conquer

Directions: "Divide" words and then "conquer" them by writing the meaning of the words. An X means the word does not have a prefix.

	prefix means	base means	word means
1. inhuman			
2. superhuman			
3. humanity	X		
4. misanthrope	*mis-* = hate		
5. philanthropic	*phil-* = love		
6. humanities	X		
7. humane	X		
	base means	**base/suffix means**	**word means**
8. anthropologist			
9. anthropomorphic		*morph* = shape, form	
10. anthropocentric		*centr* = center	

DID YOU KNOW?

Since 1976, the philanthropic organization known as Habitat for Humanity has built homes for people in over 100 countries across the world. Thousands of Americans who share a "love" for "humankind" have volunteered their time and energy to help victims of floods, earthquakes, famines, wars, and poverty. These humane volunteers, who have come from all walks of life, include President Jimmy Carter and his wife Roslyn. President Carter is widely respected as a man of great humanity. In 2002, he won the Nobel Prize for Peace.

Part B:
Combine and Create

Letter Unscramble

Directions: Unscramble the letters to make words that fill in the blanks.

There's an overpopulation of deer in our town. People are fighting about

whether it is [1]_____ or [2]_____ to

reduce the deer population.

We gave the money we raised to [3] _____for

[4] _____.

The [5]_____ [6]_____ in our town is a place

for stray cats and dogs to stay while they are waiting to be adopted.

[1] A E H M N U

[2] A E H I M N N U

[3] A A B H I T T

[4] A H I M N T U Y

[5] A E H M N U

[6] C I O S T Y E

Part C:
Read and Reason

A Conversation

Directions: Read the following conversation between a superhero and one of his fans.

Fan: "How can I learn to be like you?"

Superhero: "You already are. Every kid like yourself has the potential to do and be great things in life. You just have to find the courage and strength inside. Seek out the best for all people, all humanity. Always try your best."

Fan: "What if I have a bad day?"

Superhero: "Every humanist has a bad day every once in awhile. It's these bad days that motivate us to see what's wrong in the world and to try to fix it."

Fan: "Where did you get your superhuman powers?"

Superhero: "My own superhuman powers are specific to me. But everyone has a specific superhuman power they excel at. It's just a matter of figuring that out."

Questions:

1. What does it mean to be a *humanist*? What does this mean to *humanity*?

    _____

    _____

2. Can you think of a *superhuman* power you would like to have? What is it?

    _____

    _____

Part D:
Extend and Explore

Word Skits

Directions: Work with a partner and pick a word. Then write it on an index card. Write what it means and write an example of when you might see it. Tell classmates what root you have used. Then act out the example of when you might see the word. See if your classmates can guess the word.

human   humane   humanity   inhuman   inhumane

Part E:
Go for the Gold!

Word Search

Directions: Find and circle the words in the word search puzzle. Answers can be across, down, diagonal, or backwards.

ANTHROPOCENTRIC   ANTHROPOID   ANTHROPOLOGY
ANTHROPOMORPHIC   HUMAN   HUMANE
HUMANISM   HUMANITIES   HUMANITY
HUMANOID   SUPERHUMAN   INHUMAN
MISANTHROPE   PHILANTHROPIST   RIGHTS
SOCIETY

A	H	J	A	H	U	M	A	N	O	I	D	T	M	T
F	N	U	N	Y	T	E	I	C	O	S	D	S	I	Y
O	C	T	T	H	R	I	G	H	T	S	K	I	S	W
A	N	T	H	R	O	P	O	L	O	G	Y	P	A	N
P	L	T	R	R	P	D	U	R	M	R	Y	O	N	A
N	D	P	O	H	O	D	L	U	M	T	B	R	T	M
H	G	I	P	N	U	P	F	A	I	F	Q	H	H	U
U	U	O	O	F	A	M	O	N	E	S	E	T	R	H
M	H	N	C	P	G	M	A	M	A	N	R	N	O	R
A	L	A	E	R	O	M	U	N	O	E	Q	A	P	E
N	F	M	N	P	U	R	U	H	I	R	O	L	E	P
E	F	U	T	H	I	Y	H	H	N	S	P	I	Y	U
I	Q	H	R	S	U	G	W	T	H	I	M	H	Q	S
O	S	N	I	W	A	A	V	H	N	W	B	P	I	D
C	V	Y	C	S	E	I	T	I	N	A	M	U	H	C

Part A:
Meet the Root

Divide and Conquer

Directions: "Divide" words and then "conquer" them by writing the meaning of the words. (Hint: Number 8 has two prefixes.) An X means the word does not have a prefix.

	prefix means	base means	word means
1. comfort	_____	_____	_____
2. dynamite	X	_____	_____
3. forte	X	_____	_____
4. dynamic	X	_____	_____
5. aerodynamic	*aer(o)-* = air, wind	_____	_____
6. hydrodynamic	_____	_____	_____
7. effort	_____	_____	_____
8. discomfort	_____ _____	_____	_____
9. fortify	X	_____	_____
10. forceful	X	_____	_____

DID YOU KNOW?

Dynamite was invented in 1866 by Alfred Nobel, a Swedish industrialist and construction engineer who was looking for better ways to blast rock. Nobel discovered that mixing nitroglycerine with silica would produce a "powerful" paste that could be detonated. Because of its "strong" force, he named the substance *dynamite* from the Greek root for "power" (*dynam*).

Part B:

Combine and Create

Making Words

Directions: Work with a partner. Make as many words as you can with the *fort,*
forc word parts and the prefixes and suffixes listed below.

Prefixes: *ef-* (or *en-*), *com-*, *dis-*	Suffixes: *-ify, -less, -ible, -ment*

Part C:
Read and Reason

Advertisement

Directions: Read the following advertisement at a health club.

Dear Customers,

Happy New Year!
Each year it takes effort and hard work to keep your body healthy. This healthy lifestyle allows you to safely experience the comfort life has to offer. So, for this New Year, we want to help you fortify your strength and keep up a healthy lifestyle with a membership cost reduced by 20 percent. Please sign up for this next year as soon as possible!

New Year's Savings!
Sign up today!!!

Questions:

1.   How do people demonstrate *effort* in a health club?

   _____

   _____

2.   How will the health club help its members *fortify* their strength?

   _____

   _____

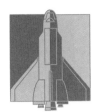

Part D:
Extend and Explore

Sentence Starters

Directions: Work with a partner to complete these sentences by selecting a word from the list. Try to put a clue about the word's meaning in your sentences. You and your partner are a team. Together choose one of the sentences to read out loud, but skip over the word. See if your classmates can guess the missing word.

fortify	fortitude	forceful	dynamic	dynamite
effort	enforcement	comfortable	discomfort	comfort

1. While I was trying to _____

_____

2. How do you know if _____

_____

3. Where in the world can _____

_____

4. What would you think about _____

_____

5. Why should _____

_____

Part E:
Go for the Gold!

Sixteen Square Wordo

Directions: Choose a free box and mark it. Then choose words from the list and write one word in each box. Your teacher will give you these words. You can choose the box for each word. Then your teacher will give a clue for each word. Mark an X in the box for each word you match to the clue. If you get four words in a row, column, diagonal, or four corners, call out, "Wordo!"

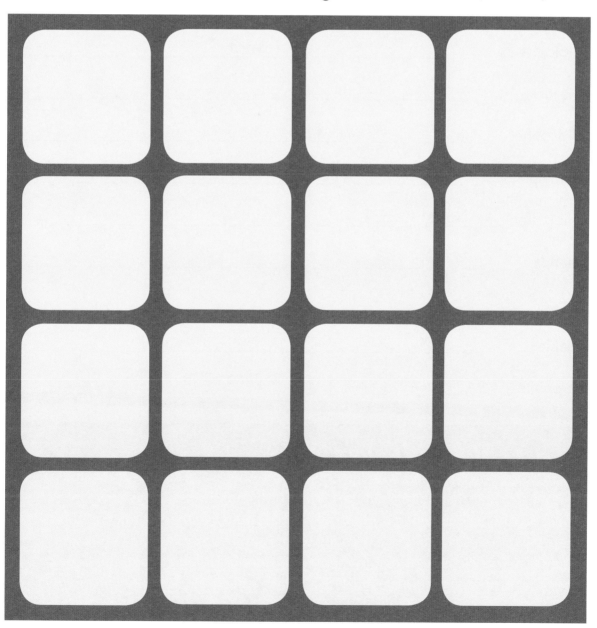

Part A:

Meet the Root

Divide and Conquer

Directions: "Divide" words and then "conquer" them by writing the meaning of the words. An X means the word does not have a prefix.

	first base means	second base means	word means
1. philanthropist	_____	_____	_____
2. philologist	_____	*log* = word	_____
3. amicable	X	_____	_____
4. philosopher	_____	*soph* = wisdom	_____
5. Philadelphia	_____	*adelphia* = brothers	_____
6. bibliophile	*bibli(o)* = book	_____	_____
7. Amanda	X	_____	_____
8. amity	X	_____	_____
9. amiable	X	_____	_____
10. audiophile	_____		

DID YOU KNOW?

William Penn was a Quaker who left England for America in search of religious freedom. In 1862, he established the colony of "Pennsylvania." This new city, Penn hoped, would become a place where all people could live together in harmony. What to name this new city? As a young man, Penn had studied the Greek and Roman classics. He now turned to them for inspiration. Penn joined the Greek words for "brothers" (*adelphia*) and "love" (*phil*), calling the new city *Philadelphia*, which means the city of "brotherly love."

Part B:
Combine and Create

Making Sentences

Directions: The Greek root *phil(o)* is often used in words about hobbies or the kinds of collections people might have. Write sentences using these *phil(o)* words.

bibliophile: a person who loves to collect books.

Sentence: _____

audiophile: a person who collects recorded music and sound systems and loves listening

Sentence: _____

_____

philologist: a person who loves words and ancient languages (especially Greek and Latin)

Sentence: _____

_____

philatelist: a person who collects stamps

Sentence: _____

_____

Part C:

Read and Reason

Dialogue

Directions: Read the following dialogue and answer the questions.

Heidi: "I'm an amateur guitar player."

Taylor: "I'm a little new at it, too. But I plan on playing in the city someday. My dad told me that a lot of musicians have started in Philadelphia, so I'm glad we live here."

Heidi: "My friend's dad is actually in the Philharmonic downtown. It has the city's best musicians. They are true lovers of music. He told me he'd introduce me to some of his friends."

Questions:

1.   What does it mean to be an *amateur* guitar player?

   _____

2.   What does it mean to be part of a *Philharmonic*?

   _____

Part D:
Extend and Explore

Authors and Illustrators

Directions: You and a partner will be a team. Write a story together using all of these words. You may use the words in any order you want, but you must use them all. Use a dictionary if necessary.

amateur   amicable   amity   amiable   amigo

_____

_____

_____

_____

_____

Now trade stories with another team. Read their story and draw a picture about some part of the story. Share your illustration and explain what you drew and why. Listen as the other team shares what they drew and why.

Part E:
Go for the Gold!

Crossword Puzzle

Directions: Read the clues below. Fill in the crossword puzzle with the correct words.

Across

1. lover of wisdom
4. a Spanish word that means "friend"
5. friendliness or goodwill between people
6. not a professional; performs for the love of the activity
7. city in Pennsylvania, known for being the city of brotherly love

Down

1. someone who makes charitable donations
2. a vine that loves trees and clings to their trunks
3. love for humankind
4. strongly attracted to or being in love with
6. peaceful relations between nations

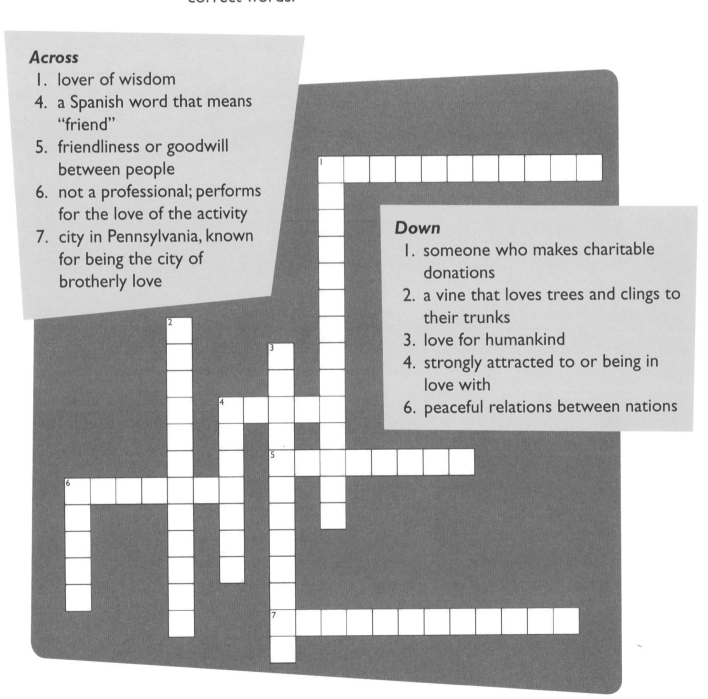

Part A:
Meet the Root

Divide and Conquer

Directions: Your teacher will give you a list of words. "Divide" words into a prefix and a base. Then "conquer" them by writing the meaning of the words.

	word	prefix means	base means	word means
1.				
2.				
3.				
4.				
5.				
6.				
7.				
8.				
9.				
10.				

Part B:
Combine and Create

Word Analysis

Directions: Look over the words from the "Divide and Conquer" activities in this unit. Then answer the questions.

1. Pick out a word whose meaning you already know. Write the word. What does it mean?

   _____

   _____

2. Pick out a word you find very interesting that you did not know before. Write the word. What does it mean? Why do you find it interesting?

   _____

   _____

3. Pick out a new word you think is very hard. Write the word. What does it mean? Tell why you think it is hard.

   _____

   _____

Part C:
Read and Reason

Poster

Directions: Read the following posting at a bookstore and answer the questions.

Notice: All Bibliophiles!

All of your favorite books are on sale!
Collect them all this weekend!

Buy rare collectors' editions!

Bring all of your philology friends and come on down to Brandon's Book Loft from noon to midnight next Saturday, March 18, 2007.

Many Greek and Latin classics are available at incredible savings!

Bring this coupon and receive 20% off one item.

Questions:

1. If *philology* means "lover of words," why does the bookstore use this term?

    _____

    _____

2. Reflecting on the advertisement, describe a *bibliophile*.

    _____

    _____

Part D:

Extend and Explore

Word Skits

Directions: With one or more partners, choose a word from "Divide and Conquer." Write the word and its definition on an index card. Now work together to create a skit to show the meaning of the word—without talking! Show your skit to others. See if they can guess your word.

Word Spokes

Part E:
Go for the Gold!

Directions: Choose one of the bases you learned in this unit. Write the base in the center of the "spokes," and brainstorm words from that base. Then choose words from your cluster for each of the directions below.

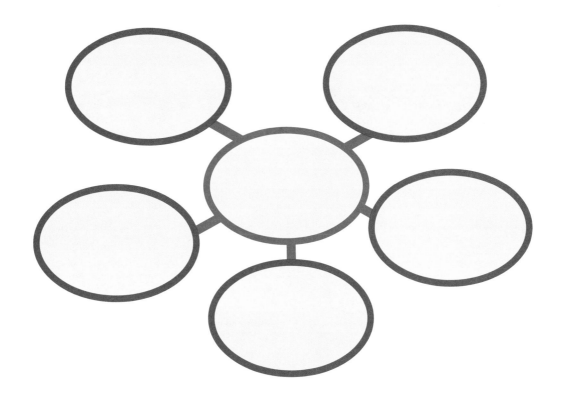

1. Pick one of the words and write **two synonyms.** _____ _____

2. Pick one of the words and write **two antonyms.** _____ _____

3. Pick one of the words and **write your own definition.** _____

_____

4. Pick one of the words and **use it in a sentence.** _____

_____

Part A:
Meet the Root

Divide and Conquer

Directions: "Divide" words and then "conquer" them by writing the meaning of
the words.

	prefix means	base means	word means
1. synchronize	_____	_____	_____
2. synthesis	_____	_____	_____
3. sympathy	_____	_____	_____
4. synthetic	_____	_____	_____
5. symphony	_____	_____	_____
6. symmetrical	_____	_____	_____
7. synonym	_____	_____	_____
8. syllable	_____	*lab* = work	_____
9. symbol	_____	*bol* = put	_____
10. synonymous	_____	_____	_____

Part B:
Combine and Create

Word Unscramble

Directions: Unscramble the letters to make words that can fill in the blanks.

If I am not wearing my glasses, I can't tell if those two lines are

[1]_____ or [2]_____.

[3]_____ are words that have similar meanings.

For example, "frigid" and "freezing" are [4]_____.

When we tell someone that we [5]_____ with

them, it means that they are in our thoughts. In fact, many

[6]_____ cards express these thoughts.

[1] A C E I L M M R S T Y

[2] A A C E I L M M R S T Y

[3] M N N O S S Y Y

[4] M N N O S S U Y Y O

[5] A E H I M P S T Y Z

[6] A H M P S T Y Y

Part C:
Read and Reason

Fill in the Blanks

Directions: Read what is on the board in Mrs. Newcomer's 5th grade math class. Fill in the blanks and answer the question below.

Today's Class

"Synthesizing Math Synonyms"

To add is also to: _____

To subtract is also to: _____

Some suggested words: compile, remove, accumulate, reduce, lessen, attach, etc.

Question:

1. To synthesize means to bring together. How does the chalk-talk above show synthesis? What is a synonym?

   _____

   _____

   _____

Part D:
Extend and Explore

Sentence Starters

Directions: Work with a partner to complete these sentences by selecting words from the list. Try to work clues for meaning into the sentences. You and your partner are a team. Together choose one of the sentences to read out loud, but skip over the added word. See if your classmates can guess the missing word.

synchronize	sympathy	symposium	syllable
synergy	synonym	symbol	symphony

1. While I was trying to _____

2. How do you know if _____

3. Where in the world can _____

4. What would you think about _____

5. Why should _____

DID YOU KNOW?

The word *symbol* comes from two Greek roots: the prefix *sym-*, which means "together," and the base *bol*, which means to "put." Its meaning can be traced to the ancient Greek practice of identifying someone by "putting" broken pottery "together." When two Greeks wanted to stay in touch, they broke a piece of pottery into halves. If one person wanted to communicate with the other, he gave his message and his broken half to a messenger. The messenger's task was to find the one person with the other broken half and "put" (*bol*) the two pieces "together" (*sym-*). By finding and "putting together" the missing half, the messenger knew for sure that he was delivering his message to the right person. A *symbol*, then, became an object that everyone knows stands for an idea. The symbol and the idea—like the broken pottery halves and the "right person"—come together in a perfect fit.

Part E:
Go for the Gold!

Word Search

Directions: Find the words listed at the bottom in the puzzle. Answers can be across, down, diagonal, or backwards.

ASYMMETRICAL	ASYMMETRY	RHYTHM	SYLLABLE
SYMBOL	SYMMETRY	SYMPATHY	SYMPHONIC
SYMPHONY	SYMPOSIUM	SYNAGOGUE	SYNCHRONIZE
SYNCOPATED	SYNERGY	SYNOD	SYNONYM
SYNONYMOUS	SYNTHESIS	SYNTHESIZE	

S	S	V	S	W	A	W	S	S	D	S	P	E	N	D
Y	I	J	O	U	P	S	Y	Y	Y	O	L	O	K	S
N	S	T	A	N	O	M	Y	N	N	B	N	H	Q	Y
C	E	Y	V	S	P	M	T	M	A	O	B	Y	V	M
H	H	Z	R	H	Y	H	Y	L	M	J	N	B	S	P
R	T	A	O	T	E	M	L	N	C	E	G	Y	E	O
O	N	N	Y	S	E	Y	M	G	O	D	T	U	M	S
N	Y	F	I	B	S	M	Y	E	C	N	G	R	F	I
I	S	Z	O	Y	N	J	M	Z	T	O	Y	P	Y	U
Z	E	K	L	T	J	Z	I	Y	G	R	P	S	R	M
E	S	Y	N	E	R	G	Y	A	S	Q	I	H	F	W
D	E	T	A	P	O	C	N	Y	S	M	Y	C	R	H
Y	H	T	A	P	M	Y	S	G	K	T	U	H	A	H
L	O	B	M	Y	S	Y	M	P	H	O	N	I	C	L
O	W	U	X	S	U	D	W	M	A	L	S	X	Y	W

Part A:
Meet the Root

Divide and Conquer

Directions: "Divide" words and then "conquer" them by writing the meaning of the words.

	prefix means	base means	word means
1. diameter	_____	_____	_____
2. diagnosis	_____	*gnos* = read, understand	_____
3. dialect	_____	*lect* = speak	_____
4. diagnostic	_____	_____	_____
5. diagram	_____	_____	_____
6. diametrical	_____	_____	_____
7. diabolical	_____	*bol* = throw	_____
8. diagonal	_____	_____	_____
9. dialogue	_____	_____	_____
10. diachronic	_____	_____	_____

Part B:
Combine and Create

Word Match

Directions: Find *dia-* words to match the definitions provided. Use words from the word bank. You may also use a dictionary if necessary.

Word Bank: diagnosis   diagonal   dialect   dialogue   diameter   diaphragm

1. A line that slants from one corner to another

   _____

2. A straight line that passes through the middle of a circle

   _____

3. A thorough examination of symptoms

   _____

4. Talking together; a conversation

   _____

5. Form of language used throughout an area or by a group of people

   _____

6. Membrane in the body between the chest and abdomen

   _____

DID YOU KNOW?

Have you ever noticed that a baby's *diaper* is always "thoroughly" white? Before disposables, babies only wore cloth *diapers*. When soiled, *diapers* were always bleached in hot water to make them white and free from germs. That's why the word *diaper* comes from two Greek roots that mean "thoroughly" (*dia-*) and "aspros" (white). Only a cloth free from bacteria is safe enough to protect the baby from rashes!

Part C:
Read and Reason

A Conversation

Directions: Read the conversation below and the directions that follow.

Teacher:	"What is the diameter of this circle?"
Don:	"Is that from one side of the circle to the other side? Or is it a diagonal line through the circle?"
Teacher:	"From one side to the other. Diagonal lines can cut across rectangles to make triangles."

Directions:

Draw a line that represents the diameter of a circle.

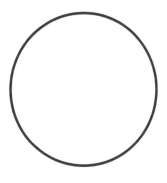

Draw a diagonal line to make two triangles out of this rectangle.

Part D:
Extend and Explore

Word Skits

Directions: Work with a partner. First, pick a word. Then write it on an index card. Also write what it means, and write an example of when you might see it. Then act out the example of when you might see the word. See if your classmates can guess the word.

dialogue   diagnosis   diagram   diagonal   diameter

DID YOU KNOW?

The word _devil_ comes from the ancient Greek word _diabolus_, which means someone who "puts" or "throws" (_bol_) hatred and slander "across" (_dia-_) an area. By the Middle Ages, other languages had adapted this word. It became _diablo_ in Spanish, _diavolo_ in Italian, _diable_ in French—and devil in English! Today we use the word _diabolical_ to describe any wicked behavior that seeks to destroy something good.

Crossword

Directions: Read the clues below. Fill in the crossword puzzle with the correct words. Use the Word Bank to help.

Across

4. a conversation
5. a membrane stretched through the midriff
6. a baby's undergarment
7. a metabolic disorder that causes frequent urination
8. a watery discharge that flows through a person

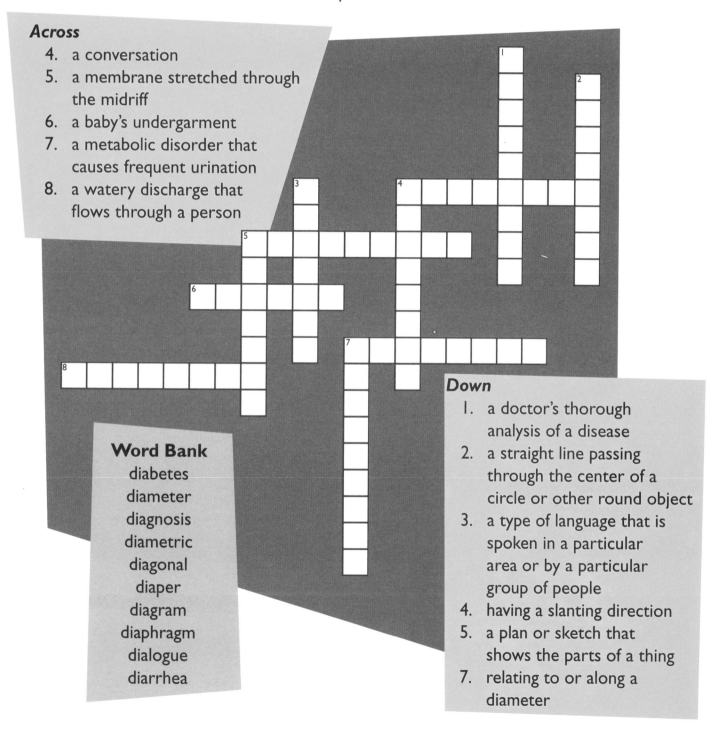

Down

1. a doctor's thorough analysis of a disease
2. a straight line passing through the center of a circle or other round object
3. a type of language that is spoken in a particular area or by a particular group of people
4. having a slanting direction
5. a plan or sketch that shows the parts of a thing
7. relating to or along a diameter

Word Bank

diabetes
diameter
diagnosis
diametric
diagonal
diaper
diagram
diaphragm
dialogue
diarrhea

Part A:
Meet the Root

Divide and Conquer

Directions: "Divide" words and then "conquer" them by writing the meaning of the words.

	prefix means	base means	word means
1. circumference	_____	_____	_____
2. perimeter	_____	_____	_____
3. peripheral	_____	_____	_____
4. circumnavigate	_____	_____	_____
5. circumstances	_____	*stanc* = stand	_____
6. periscope	_____	_____	_____
7. pericardium	_____	_____	_____
8. circumambulate	_____	_____	_____
9. periodontics	_____	_____	_____
10. circumlocution	_____	*locut* = speak	_____

Part B:
Combine and Create

Word Sort

Directions: Sometimes *peri-* means "around," and sometimes it doesn't. Put these words on the chart where they belong.

perimeter   peril   periscope   perish   periodic

periwinkle   periphery   perilous   periodical   perishable

means "around"	does not mean "around"

DID YOU KNOW?

The word *circus* comes from ancient Rome, where games and animal acts were performed in a round, enclosed field shaped like a modern sports track. Rome's first and most famous *circus*, the "Circus Maximus" (the largest circle), could seat 300,000 people! The most famous American *circus*, called the "Greatest Show on Earth," began in 1871 and traveled around the country. Today it is still traveling as the "Ringling Brothers and Barnum and Bailey Circus." Centuries later, we still recall the "roundness" of the Roman original *circus* when we say that an event takes place "under the big top" or is like "a three-ring circus."

Part C:

Read and Reason

Read and Respond

Directions: Read the following beginning to a
short story and answer the questions.

> Every month or so, the ice-cream truck makes a periodic
> visit to our neighborhood. After driving around the
> peripheral roads, the truck eventually turns onto our
> street. The truck has huge side-view mirrors to give the
> driver good peripheral vision. That way, he can see all
> the children who are rushing to buy his fudge bars.

Questions:

1. How might side-view mirrors improve a driver's *peripheral* vision?

   _____

   _____

2. Explain what is meant by the phrase *peripheral roads*. Describe what the
   driver might have seen as he drove "around the peripheral roads."

   _____

   _____

   _____

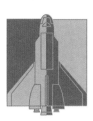

Part D:
Extend and Explore

"Timed" Word Trees

Directions: Work with a partner to fill the tree with *peri-* or *circum-* words. You and your partner are a team. The team that brainstorms the most words and definitions will win! First, select the word part you are going to work with. Then follow the directions.

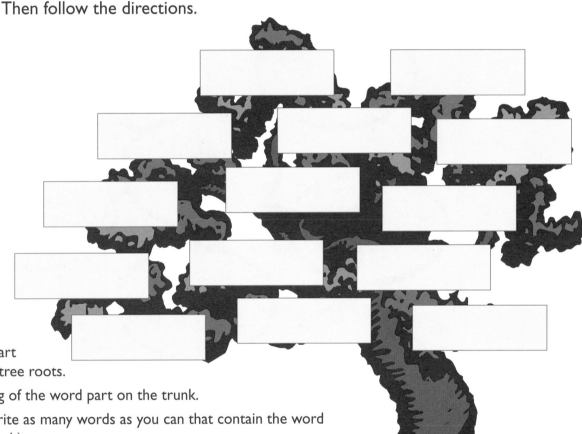

1. Write the word part you chose on the tree roots.

2. Write the meaning of the word part on the trunk.

3. In two minutes, write as many words as you can that contain the word part (one per branch).

4. Trade papers with your partner.

5. On a separate sheet of paper, write the meaning of as many of your partner's words as you can in two minutes.

6. How many different words and definitions did your team come up with? (If the same word was on both your trees, only count it once!)

Part E:
Go for the Gold!

Word Spokes

Directions: Choose a different *circum-, circu-* word from your cluster for each of the directions below.

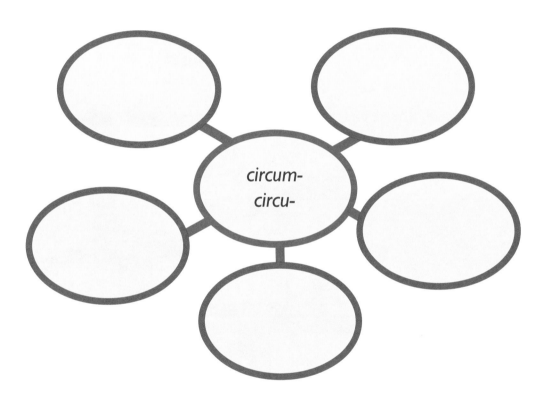

circum-
circu-

1. Pick one of the words and write **two synonyms.** _____ _____

2. Pick one of the words and write **two antonyms.** _____ _____

3. Pick one of the words and **write your own definition.** _____

   _____

4. Pick one of the words and **use it in a sentence.** _____

   _____

Part A:
Meet the Root

Divide and Conquer

Directions: Your teacher will give you a list of words. "Divide" words into a prefix and a base. Then "conquer" them by writing the meaning of the words.

	word	prefix means	base means	word means
1.	_____	_____	_____	_____
2.	_____	_____	_____	_____
3.	_____	_____	_____	_____
4.	_____	_____	_____	_____
5.	_____	_____	_____	_____
6.	_____	_____	_____	_____
7.	_____	_____	_____	_____
8.	_____	_____	_____	_____
9.	_____	_____	_____	_____
10.	_____	_____	_____	_____

Part B:
Combine and Create

Paragraph Writing

Directions: Work with a partner. Select one group of words. Write a paragraph that includes each word in the group. Provide some clues about which words you have used, but leave blanks for the words themselves. Then trade paragraphs with another group. Ask others to try to fill in your blanks.

circumference	diagnosis	symbol
perimeter	diagnostic	synonym
diameter	diabetes	syllable
diagonal	circulation	syllogism

Part C:
Read and Reason

Read the Passage

Directions: Read the passage below and answer the questions that follow.

On July 4, 1776, the 13 American colonies made a bold step for independence from England by adopting a document they called "The Unanimous Declaration of the Thirteen United States of America." Written by Thomas Jefferson, this "Declaration of Independence" expressed their belief that all human beings are endowed by their Creator with "certain unalienable rights." Because they believed those "unalienable rights" were not being respected, the colonists came together and made this famous declaration:

We hold these truths to be self-evident, that all men are created equal, that they are endowed by their Creator with certain unalienable rights, that among these are Life, Liberty, and the pursuit of Happiness.

Think about the word *hold* in this statement. Did you know that a belief that you hold close to your heart is called a tenet? This famous statement expresses the essential tenets upon which our American government was founded and that the government continues to protect today. When we believe in our tenets, we "hold" onto them for life!

Questions:

1. Think of a *tenet* or belief that you hold dear. What is it? Why is it so important to you?

   _____

2. What do you think the word *unalienable* means? What roots (prefix and suffix) do you recognize?

   _____

3. Do you recognize a "Latin number" in the words *unanimous* and *united*? What is it? Explain what you think the words *unanimous* and *united* mean. _____

   _____

4. Do you recognize the Latin base *vid* in the word *self-evident*? What does it mean? Explain what you think self-evident means. Share your *tenet* with a friend. Then check your definitions in a dictionary.

   _____

   _____

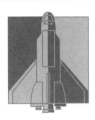

Part D:
Extend and Explore

Sixteen Square Wordo

Directions: Choose a free box and mark it. Then choose words from the list and write one word in each box. Your teacher will give you these words. You can choose the box for each word. Then your teacher will give a clue for each word. Mark an X in the box for each word you match to the clue. If you get four words in a row, column, diagonal, or four corners, call out, "Wordo!"

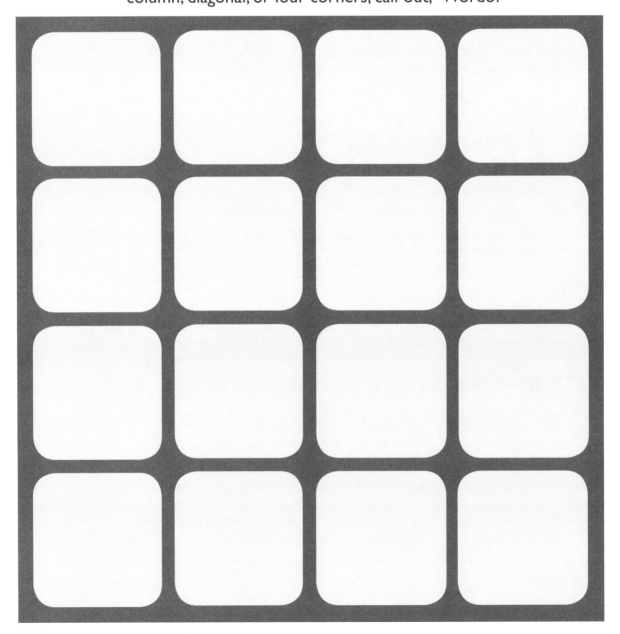

A Final Reflection

Part E:
Go for the Gold!

Congratulations! You have finished this whole book! Now look back and choose the three roots you liked best. Write them down and tell why they are your favorites!

My Favorite Roots

1. _____

I like this root because _____

2. _____

I like this root because _____

3. _____

I like this root because _____

Hooray! You Did it!

Now pick out three new words you learned that you think are interesting. Write the words and tell why they are your favorites.

Most Interesting Words

1. _____

I think this is an interesting word because _____

_____

2. _____

I think this is an interesting word because _____

_____

3. _____

I think this is an interesting word because _____

_____

Now compare your choices with those of your friends! Did you pick any of the same roots and interesting words?

#10656 Building Vocabulary from Word Roots